/   Aginsky, B.W.
970.3   Deep valley.

595

935970

Deep Valley

Deep Valley

❧

BY BURT W. AND ETHEL G. AGINSKY

❧

❧

Santa Clara County Free Library
San Jose. California

🕭 STEIN AND DAY/*Publishers*/New York

Designed by Bernard Schleifer
Printed in the United States of America
Stein and Day/*Publishers*/7 East 48 Street, New York, N.Y. 10017

to Franz Boas and Ruth Benedict

Preface

IT IS with some amount of reluctance that we present this volume to the public because it is an innovation that we fear may be misunderstood and thought to be a fictional account rather than the result of twenty-five years of library and field research. However, we feel that the value of showing an American aboriginal culture in a form in which the people act and speak as they did previous to white contact warrants the attempt.

Every situation described, every individual speaking, is the reflection of a reality which existed as of about the time that the first intensive contact with the white man began.

Much of the material was taken down phonetically and then translated by a number of informants who did not know that it was being checked. Accounts of all kinds of events were also checked with informants who had been present when the event had occurred.

These people had no writing, but they had trained their memories to so great an extent and had so ritualized almost every action that we have many cases where exact wording obtained from one Indian pertaining to a conversation which had occurred in his youth was also given to us by other Indians who were present during that same event. One of the best examples of the memory training of these people is that a professional, i.e., a doctor, gambler, religico, or fisherman, memorized well over a thousand songs which he had to use in exact combination to bring about desired results.

The authors have published articles in scientific journals and monographs which have resulted from their study. The material in those monographs and articles has been incorporated in this book. A list of the titles will be found in the bibliography.

More has been published on the aboriginal culture of the Pomo Indians by competent anthropologists, historians, and other scientists, than on any other aboriginal group which has come to the authors' attention. All previously published material has been checked by the authors while in the field.

Many monographs reflect the fieldworker's attempt to establish uniformities of action in non-literate tribes to the point where the population is presented as being stereotyped. All act the same. We found that discrepancies between and among authors, for the most part, were not discrepancies at all, but reports of different types of activity and behavior, and that the individual had a choice when certain events occurred.

The reader will find no footnotes in the body of the book although all published material was checked during our research in the field. To include footnotes would mean to have at least a few thousand. E. W. Gifford's *Element List* alone contains almost a thousand items. If we referred to the various authors who have written and to the various informants who gave us our information, it would defeat the purpose of making the presentation real to the reader.

Aside from the various researchers who are listed in the bibliography there were thirty-two scientists who worked on this project under the supervision of and in conjunction with the authors. These thirty-two individuals represented the many social sciences known today. They have contributed to the total study.

The library research started as an assignment pertaining to the social organization of these people in a class of Ruth Benedict's at Columbia University in 1932. The library research continued until 1934 when Professor Franz Boas of Columbia University sponsored a field trip with a grant from the Social Science Research Council of Columbia University. A second trip was sponsored by Ruth Benedict in 1935 and 1936. It was during these field trips that our focus was upon a reconstruction of the aboriginal culture in the prewhite days. A rather large number of old Indian men and women who remembered the Spaniards in that area were still alive. Some still have Spanish names and in those years many spoke some amount of Spanish.

While on these field trips we became interested in the total history of the meeting of diverse cultures and the results as found in the population, especially in regard to population interaction which has become so vital a matter in the world today. For here, in this area of northern California, we found a case history of the clash of empires in the modern world. This was the last frontier, where the

Russian empire established a post at Fort Ross in 1811. The Spaniards felt this an encroachment and so established missions north of San Francisco Bay at Solano in 1823. Freeman raised the first American flag in 1848. The letters written to Madrid and Moscow by the Spaniards and Russians and the reports to London by the English who were established in the northwest and by the Yankee traders who saw a rich area, all indicated that this was the meeting ground. The people of this area were pawns in the game of world politics and those who manipulated the pawns were for the most part so distant from their home governments that they had almost free hands in their actions.

It is here in this area that we have in a short time span a series of contacts. 1852 was the year of the first white settlement in the valley of which we speak. The first newspaper was established but two or three years later, and the complete files are available for study. Thus with a combination of all the written records, the court records, and the personal recounting of the history by both whites and Indians, the opportunity is present to study the change from a "primitive" tribe to a modern civilization with its mass agriculture, lumbering, industry, transportation, and the other concomitants of our everyday world.

It was for these reasons, as well as many others, that the Social Science Field Laboratory was organized by the authors under the sponsorship of New York University in 1939, for the purpose of an interdisciplinary study of this community. Group field trips were made in 1939, '40, and '41, when they were discontinued because of the war. They were resumed in 1947 under the auspices of the Social Science Field Laboratory and Syracuse University and again in 1948. During the interim, members of the Laboratory remained in the field for as much as fourteen months at a time. The authors returned to the field to resurvey the situation and do field work in 1946. Thus there have been three main periods of study in the field, from 1934-1936, 1939-1942, and 1946 to the present time.

Funds for this work have been supplied by the Columbia University Social Science Research Council, New York University, The Social Science Research Council, Syracuse University, and especially the Wenner-Gren Foundation for Anthropological Research (formerly the Viking Fund), as well as from many private sources.

The reader will notice that names are infrequently used. This has been done because the aboriginal Pomo refrains from using names as much as possible. Real names were sacred and were kept secret. Nicknames were used, but even then the individual was always wary lest he make a slip and give away the sacred name of one of his relatives or indicate that he knew the name of a non-relative, for that would have been an invitation to be poisoned by the man whose name he had used inadvertently.

The Indians consistently used age or status terms to indicate the individual about whom they were speaking, e.g., "that old man," or "the old man who lives near the hill," or "that young girl," or "the singer," or "the gambler." This was done because each individual in all except a few cases was dealt with and referred to as a member of a status group.

Many ethnographies have been published. This book can also be classed as an ethnography, minus abstractions but plus human relations. It can be compared with the report by a geographer who describes a particular area without comment as to what is of value in contradistinction to a geologist who reports the kinds of rock formation and names them.

Thus the reader will find that there is every attempt in this volume to present the culture of those people only as that culture functioned and as it was taught to the younger members, or as incidents were discussed against a background of the culture by the people themselves.

There is no question but that a certain amount of the personality of the authors has been involved. This is especially true in regard to the selection of the characters, situations, and so on. Otherwise the presentation of this culture would take at least ten heavy volumes. In this regard it would be worthwhile noting Barrett's short paper on Pomo Bear Doctors.

Portions of this book have been read by an old Indian who has made a study of his own people. He passed upon the work and made only a few suggestions as to choice of words here and there.

There are many reasons why we have waited to present this study, the most important of which is that it is only of late that the really old informants have died and can no longer become involved because they divulged personal, dangerous, and secret material. Their descendants are still alive; every attempt has been made to disguise the individual characters in the book so that no person will be recognized. Thus names have been interchanged.

Too frequently monographs have been presented in such a way that the individuals in the population become stereotyped. Paul Radin in his *Crashing Thunder* set a departure by presenting the individual. The main attempt in this book is along those lines. But there has been in addition a careful presentation of interpersonal relations, the reactions of individuals to events and occurrences, the positive and negative reactions and thoughts of individuals to the structures of their culture, and the incipient and actual rebellions which occurred.

The authors became more and more aware of the fundamental anthropological finding that human beings are human beings, basically the same, but varying in their personalities and cultures. It was this which made the work fascinating and which made the tedious concentration upon detail worthwhile. when it became almost overwhelming. To sit with an aged man or woman for hours gradually leading the conversation to a specific incident, which had occurred sixty or more years previously, can be fascinating as a game, and it was a game at first. But later it became nerve-wracking waiting for the information to be volunteered conversationally. There were times when attempts were made to short cut, and a few times the short cut speeded up the obtaining of information. But that occurred only rarely since the old people resented any knowledge of intimate details of their lives even when it had been volunteered by them. We found it was best to disremember and act interested whenever the informant repeated some incident or story. The repetition indicated importance, but there were times when the informant would say, "I told you that two years ago." However they were of the old tradition where repetition was not only acceptable, but was consciously indulged in in order to bring about the sharp memorization so essential for living in that world of theirs so full of anxiety and fear. It must be remembered that they had no books, no libraries, and no pictures.

The refinement of research techniques is of great importance whether it be in the natural or the social sciences. In the process of checking the information it was found as has been found before, that the age, sex, occupation, family affiliation, playgroup affiliation, and so on, were very important. Thus a plural number of informants were used from every category and combination of categories possible. Not only the thoughts, beliefs, and attitudes were reported, but the activities as well, and it was found that frequently there was a difference. The modal person was used as well as the deviant and the extreme deviants, both positive and negative.

In short, the value of a study of this kind and the presentation of the facts as such, must be weighed in relation to the refined techniques of research. This is, perhaps, another step forward in the direction of science.

Perhaps the presentation, true to life, of one case of a people who live an holistic life of their own, ecologically adjusted to their geographic, cultural, and intertribal environment, may make clear that the American Indian did not live a simple life, was not a barbarian and a savage, or ignorant. And perhaps, of most importance, this book may interest people in reading further in the field of anthropology and social science where lies the solution to this modern living in a complex world constantly being rent by intercultural strife, subjugation, and turmoil.

These Indians lived a full functioning existence before the coming of the whites. The advent of the whites resulted in disenfranchisement, disintegration, and chaos for the population. The effects are still evident today.

The mutual respect for one another's backgrounds and cultures in a world which has become small because of increased communication and transportation is of paramount importance and from all indications will remain so for some time to come.

Acknowledgments

Initial research was begun on this subject in 1932. Field work started in 1934 and continued through 1936; it was done in conjunction with the Social Science Research Council of Columbia University, under the supervision of the Anthropology Department. The first joint social science research was begun in 1939 under supervision of the Social Science Field Laboratory (B. W. and E. G. Aginsky, Directors) in conjunction with New York University Graduate School, and was continued until 1941, when it was interrupted by the war. Field work resumed in 1946; this time it was made possible by a grant from The Wenner-Gren Foundation for Anthropological Research (formerly The Viking Fund). In 1947, the Social Science Field Laboratory was reactivated with the aid of an additional grant from The Wenner-Gren Foundation. This field research, which was continued during the summer of 1948, was done in conjunction with the Maxwell Graduate School of Syracuse University.

Altogether, thirty-two scientists, representing various social sciences, cooperated in this integrated study of a community. (Cf. Bibliography for other publications on this study.)

Thanks are due to The Wenner-Gren Foundation for Anthropological Research (formerly The Viking Fund), The Social Science Research Council, The Social Science Research Council of Columbia University, New York University, Syracuse University, and private donors who made the work possible.

The authors also wish to thank the "Transography Institute" (The Institute for World Understanding of Peoples, Cultures and Languages), for the funds for secretarial and editorial help.

Our many friends in Ukiah were helpful in so many ways that we cannot fully express our appreciation. Special gratitude goes to Zella and George Bartlett, who contributed immeasurably to the study. Mr. Charles Mannon and Mr. Paul Poulos aided in many different areas of the work. The Public Library was always cooperative and ready to facilitate research. And there are many Pomo Indians, as well as townspeople and ranchers, who, although too numerous to list individually, are remembered by us with gratitude and affection.

Many members of the Anthropology Department at the University of California at Berkeley, especially Alfred L. Kroeber, Cora DuBois, and Edward Gifford, must also be thanked. It was Alfred Kroeber, a former teacher of ours, who suggested that we run to earth vague references to poisoning that each Pomo denied for himself but attributed to others.

Introduction:
The Year Was 1934

WE drove northward along the Russian River, toward the low mountains that had been visible for some time. Soon the road branched away and upward from the water. The car labored as we began the ascent; the road climbed, twisting and turning until it cut through a narrow pass.

Suddenly a beautiful valley, completely encircled by mountains, opened below us. It lay like a park surrounded by steep brown and tawny velvet hills. The valley floor was a golden carpet, with ancient dark green oak trees evenly set about; it was cultivated land, in a variety of colors and geometric designs, seemingly planned by man to enhance the valley's natural beauty. The Russian River, with its green borders of shrubbery and trees, bisected the valley from north to south.

A short ride brought us to a rather typical northern Californian town, halfway between modernity and the horse and buggy days. Along the main street were the usual chain stores— Montgomery-Ward, J. C. Penney, the dime stores, as well as churches of several denominations, a movie house, one modern and a few rather ancient hotels, some restaurants, gasoline stations, and bars. Trees lined the streets; the houses represented a mixture of styles from all parts of the United States. Examples of modified Southern colonial, New England clapboard, Victorian, and other architectural types, gave the town an unmistakable American look. There seemed little enough in this ordinary American community to rouse special interest or curiosity.

Its prosperous farms, orchards, and vineyards, thriving stores, well-kept streets and public park, as well as the fact that it provided its own power, light, and other facilities, all gave it an air of being what it in fact was—a progressive but not unusual community.

It was early in the summer of 1934. Every morning the sun rose from behind the mountains like a ball of fire in the cool morning air. It moved slowly across the cloudless sky toward the mountains to the west until the temperature at high noon reached one hundred degrees and more in the shade. The nights, however, were cool and invigorating.

The townspeople were friendly and helpful to us in our investigations. Their backgrounds and traditions were varied—some were descendants of the Forty-Niners of the gold-rush days. Others were said to be descendants of the early outlaws who sought sanctuary in these mountains until the chase had been dropped and their misdeeds forgotten. Others were the descendants of several generations of westward migrating pioneers. There was also a large group of Italian immigrants and their families, who had lived in the valley, cultivated the vineyards, and made wine for over forty years. Some of the largest and best known American wineries had vineyards in this valley. Five wineries were also located in the valley proper. There was a sprinkling of Japanese and Chinese, a few Negroes, and a mixture of late European immigrants, as well as some Filipinos and Mexicans.

The oldest residents were the Pomo Indians. There were three Indian settlements, called Rancherias, in the valley. This name was given them by the Spaniards, who had been the earliest "Western" residents in this locality.

Indians worked side by side with whites in the orchards and in the hopfields; their coloration varied considerably, from near-white to characteristically Indian. There appeared to be an admirable congeniality and community spirit among the workers.

Our first impression was of a well-adjusted population and community with few tension points that might be disruptive to a peaceful and fruitful life in these beautiful surroundings.

Everyone seemed eager to cooperate with us in our investigations, and ranchers allowed their Indian employees to spend time with us even though they were needed in the fields.

Some of the Indians were already known to us by name from previous anthropological reports, and these we sought out for help in filling in the picture of the old Indian culture. One day we located Maimi, a fine-looking woman, fair in coloring, and neatly dressed. In order that she might speak more freely than she could at her camp, where numerous relatives sat around listening, we took her to the park in town and talked with her there. At noon we drove to a roadside stand on the fringe of town, and ordered hamburgers. The proprietor, to our astonishment, said, "I don't serve Indians."

This was the first indication of prejudice in the community. We soon learned that only one restaurant in town served Indians —it was owned by a Chinese—that Indians could sit only in the balcony of the movie house, did not attend church in town nor have any job in town, and attended segregated schools. In general, a rigid caste system prevailed in which many of the people of the community participated.

The three Indian Rancherias, each some distance from the city limits, looked very much like the areas "on the other side of the tracks" in many small American cities—full of dirty unkempt yards, dilapidated houses, and sour-faced, uncommunicative residents. These Indians were described to us in several denigrating ways by some of the white townspeople: "The lowest and dirtiest Indians in America. Diggers."

"They are dumb, stupid, dirty, ignorant, lazy, and no-good."

"As soon as they get their hands on some money they all get drunk. When they get drunk they knife and kill each other."

"Every time they earn some money they spend it. They are always in debt."

"So you are going to study the Indians? Well, you won't get them to talk. Even if you do, they don't know anything."

Others, however, said in actual words, and in effect, "These Indians are fine people. I was brought up with them. We played together as children. If it were not for them we would have a hard time during the harvest. They work in the hot sun all day,

17

children and old men and women so feeble they have to sit while they work. Sure, they get drunk once in a while, but so do the whites."

Others said, "Give these people a chance and they will be all right."

The Indians, for their part, had as much to say about the whites; for example: "They stole our land and now they won't even pay us enough to live."

"They won't even let us gather the acorns that fall on the ground and that used to be our main food supply. They chase us away and let their pigs eat them or let them just rot."

"We can't hunt for deer out of season."

"They won't give us a job in town."

Others said amelioratingly, "'Some of the whites are O.K. They help us out during the winter and once in a while they give us a break."

An old Indian, who in 1935 was approximately one hundred twelve years of age, summed up much of the Indians' thought on the subject. He said, "What is man? A man is nothing. Without his family he is of less importance than that bug crossing the trail, of less importance than spit or dung. At least they can be used to help poison a man. A man must be with his family to amount to anything with us. If he had nobody else to help him, the first trouble he got into he would be killed by his enemies because there would be no relatives to help him fight the poison of the other group. No woman would marry him because her family would not let her marry a man with no family. He would be poorer than a newborn child; he would be poorer than a worm and the family would not consider him worth anything. He would not bring renown or glory with him. He would not bring support of other relatives either. The family is important. If a man has a large family and a profession and upbringing by a family that is known to produce good children, then he is somebody, and every family is willing to have him marry a woman of their group. It is the family that is important. In the white way of doing things, the family is not so important. The police and soldiers take care of protecting you, the courts give you justice, the post office carries messages for you, the school

18

teaches you. Everything is taken care of, even your children, if you die; but with us the family must do all of that.

"Without the family we are nothing, and in the old days before the white people came, the family was given the first consideration by anyone who was about to do anything at all. That is why we got along. We had no courts, judges, schools, and the other things you have, but we got along better than you. We had poison, but if we minded our own business and restrained ourselves, we lived well. We were taught to leave people alone. We were taught to consider that others had to live. We were taught that we would suffer from the devil, spirits, and ghosts or other people if we did not support one another. The family was everything, and no man ever forgot that. Each person was nothing; but as a group, joined by blood, the individual knew that he would get the support of all his relatives if anything happened. He also knew that if he was a bad person the head man of his family would pay another tribe to kill him so that there would be no trouble afterward and so that he would not get the family into trouble all of the time.

"That is why we were good people and why we were friends with the white people when they came. But the white people were different from us. They wanted to take the world for themselves. My grandfather told me that the white people were homeless and had no families. They came by themselves and settled on our property. They had no manners. They did not know how to get along with other people. They were strangers who were rough and common and did not know how to behave. But I have seen that these people of yours are even worse. They have taken everything away from the Indians, and they take everything away from each other. They do not help one another when they are in trouble, and they do not care what happens to other people. We were not like that. We would not let a person die of starvation when we had plenty of food. We would not bury our dead with no show. We would kill another person by poisoning him if he was an enemy, but we would not treat a stranger the way they treat their own brothers and sisters. Your people are hard to understand. My brother lived with your people for twenty years, and he said that he was used to you,

19

but he cannot understand yet why you people act as you do. You are all the same in one way. We are all the same in another. "What is wrong with you? The white people have the land. They own the courts, they own everything, but they will not give the Indians enough money to live on. It is hard to understand.

"With us, the family was everything. Now it is nothing. We are getting like the white people, and it is bad for the old people. We had no old people's homes like you. The old people were important. They were wise. Your old people must be fools."

With growing familiarity, a history of this community unfolds that is as colorful as any novel ever presented. Events came to light that are as cruel, wanton, and bloody as any recorded in history—dogged manhunts, brutal segregation, slow starvation— all the results of man's inhumanity to man.

This is the area of northernmost penetration by the Spaniards, who slaughtered, raped, and enslaved these people. It is the area of southernmost penetration by the Tsarist Russians, who first came to the territory via Alaska as fur traders and who established a settlement and gave their name to the river. The Russians treated the Indians as equals, intermarried with them, and, when they finally left and went back to their own country, took their "native" wives and children with them.

This is the area first discovered by Sir Francis Drake in 1579, and so picturesquely described in his account of the journey. It is this same area in which the American people as well as their government consistently exterminated, exploited, and persecuted the native Indians. It is still a fascinating community about whose history many of the present non-Indian members know little, and on which they look with little interest and less understanding.

We soon found the same problems here that confront the world at large, differing only in particulars. This one valley offers some insight by means of which some understanding may be achieved of our present world beset with the problems of minority groups, civil liberties, and the insistence of peoples seeking enfranchisement. The magnitude of the problems to be solved has been thrust on all peoples, regardless of their geographic location or color.

We are cognizant, in the United States, of the Negro movement. However, it can be multiplied by a number of minority groups in America and especially by a number of American Indian populations, the original inhabitants who, according to report, represent the severest cases of deprivation.

In every case studied by us (American Indians and the many other minority groups, studied both in America and in their ancestral habitats either through field research or library research), it becomes evident that members of any one of the present situations are not to be censured for the action of their ancestors. They are neither better nor worse than the rest of us, who are too occupied by our own affairs to investigate the situation in our nation and to understand present conditions in historical perspective. However, censure should be expressed when people are cognizant of the conditions and help to perpetuate rather than alleviate them.

Our first field trip was but 82 years after the first important contact with westerners. This was indeed a short period of time when compared with the 440 years of contact in the Caribbean, and the 300 years of contact of the English in New England. We might say that many westerners' derogatory opinions of these Indians was due to a lack of knowledge of what the Pomo were like before contact. They had solved problems of group living, two of which constitute pressing matters in the world today. One is that of population explosion, and the other is that of psychiatric help without segregation.

The presentation of the ancestral culture of the Pomo Indians may be duplicated by that of the Irish, the many African, Puerto Rican, and other minority groups presently in the United States. It is hoped that the picture of the Pomo Indians previous to white contact may aid in some understanding of the total subject matter.

It is also the hope of the authors that the book will help to correct the picture of the American Indian as a naked horseback warrior.

Chapter 1

IN the sweathouse the coals glowed in the firepit, casting a warm light on the faces of the old men and a few old women who sat close around them, absorbing the heat no longer supplied by their bodies. Farther from the fire the younger men were engaged in lively conversation. Latecomers, returning from their evening meals at home, entered and seated themselves among the rest.

The end-of-the-day quietness had settled on the valley; it was the time for enjoying the friendliness and comfort of the sweathouse.

Deerhunter leaned forward, stirred the coals, and placed some wood upon the fire. He settled himself comfortably back and to his old man neighbor said thoughtfully, "I cannot forget those stories I heard from the Lower Lake people last year when I was on the trading expedition. They come back to my mind very often!"

Some of the younger men sitting nearby overheard him and stopped talking in order to listen.

Deerhunter was one of the most honored and feared men of the tribe, not only because of his great age, but because he had been a successful money manufacturer as well as deer hunter. He was, in addition, the Head of one of the largest families in the valley.

Aged One replied, "Yes, I, too, often think about those troubling stories. But what happened, happened far away. We all know that the creatures from the south are dangerous and

23

steal our people away. But in the past they have only taken the essence, never the bodies."

Man of Many Beads, one of the young men sitting nearby, listened intently, for he had also been on the trading expedition, also remembered the stories, and had himself been moved to think about them often. Another young man, Wakim, asked, "I have heard only fragments of the stories. Tell us exactly what it was you heard."

"The Lower Lake men told us," Man of Many Beads replied, "that shortly before we arrived, strange creatures had come from the south; they resembled our supernaturals, but were somehow different. They came in a group. From a distance, some appeared to be very tall, with two heads, one high above and one lower down in front, with a tail behind. Those had four legs. Some had a shiny skin which glinted in the sun.

"The Lake people gathered together and performed rituals and made offerings to avert danger, but when the strange creatures drew near they turned into men, some of whom were mounted on animals much larger than deer, with no antlers. The men carried thunder and smoke that could kill from a distance. Among themselves they spoke a language which the men of Lower Lake could not understand. They had with them one man who spoke somewhat as the Lower Lake people did and who was kin to the wife of one of the Lower Lake men."

"Yes, that is true," said Deer Hunter, "they had the power of Gilyak, and they killed many of the Lower Lake people. Not only that, but many acted like Coyote. When they changed into men, they raped the women, most of whom were too terrified to resist. They ate huge quantities of food, and when they left took with them many of the young people."

"What happened to the young people?" asked Wakim.

"That we do not know, except for two young men who later escaped and made their way back to Lower Lake. They said that these creatures were really men who were cruel and fierce. The group had been taken south for three days, all of them tied together, and it was not until the third night that these two had escaped." Deer Hunter paused.

"The dead are always taken to the South," Aged One said, "for that is where Gilyak lives. They must have been the supernaturals, not mere men. You know those Lake Country people are not good people. They have had much trouble, for they do not take care of the supernaturals nor perform their ceremonies properly. These are the things that happen when people stop being careful and conscientious."

"That is true," replied another. "Some of their old men said as much at the time. Aiii, but that was the wrong time for us to arrive. They were all in mourning, unhappy, and it was difficult for them to receive us suitably. There was a scarcity of food, and the money we had brought for making purchases was no longer of much interest to them."

"If they were men," continued Aged One, "then how could they behave like that? Are they the same as those on the coast who have come into our valley from across the waters to the north for fur? They too kill at a distance and carry thunder and smoke."

"They cannot be the same," an old man answered, "for those people have never taken anything away from us. We have exchanged presents with them, and when they kill they kill only animals."

"Yet when they first came, the coast people also thought that they were being visited by supernaturals. Now all know they are men like ourselves but from a different tribe of people," said Aged One. "Those strangers at Lower Lake acted more like the supernaturals. The Lake People have done bad things and are being punished. They have not prayed, they have broken taboos, they have not done sufficient homage to the supernaturals."

The finality in the old man's voice was like a signal: the focus of attention dissolved and all over the sweathouse separate conversations began again.

To the inhabitants of Deep Valley the sweathouse was a combination community meetinghouse, old people's clubhouse, newspaper, movie house, bar, sanctuary, and retreat. This was the place where the men of all ages, and some old women, could get out from underfoot of the active women, who, in effect, owned the dwelling houses and ran them with uncontested authority.

It was at the sweathouse that gamblers, doctors, deerhunters

25

and all other professional men lived during the "fixing" for participation in their professions. A "fixing" required four days of fasting, prayers, and rituals; these made a professional "powerful," his power being absorbed from the supernaturals; to go near fresh meat or fish, a pregnant or menstruating woman, or in fact a woman of sexually ripe age, would not only invalidate his power, but make him ill. It would also cause the death of an unborn child, bring illness and death to infants and children, and, in general, hardship to all concerned. To touch a man who was "fixed" was dangerous to the toucher, whether he were relative or stranger.

The sweathouse was also a place of sanctuary from a nagging wife, for women could only send messages to their husbands through a third person, and these could be ignored. It was, essentially, the men's house, but a few old women were tolerated, those who had a keen wit, wisdom, and a reputation for being almost men—that is to say, well beyond their menopause.

Youths who disrupted the community were punished here by being made to carry a certain number of armloads of wood for the fire. If that did not subdue a youth's exuberance and confine his spirit to worthwhile pursuits, an old man would place a hot coal in the boy's hand and close his own hand over it, a process usually sufficient to make a model individual of the most recalcitrant. This was punishment meted out not by a member of the family, but rather by the old fire tender or some other honored man, at the request of the older relatives of the youth, for it was customary to refrain from acts that might antagonize one's relatives.

It was in the sweathouse that the young men learned of the place of a man in the community and his oneness with it. This relationship was in contrast with the intensity of the in-group attitudes of the extended family, in which the oldest male and female, each with his and her own prerogatives and duties, ruled primarily in the interests of the family's well-being rather than that of the total population.

The sweathouse was especially important to the men since the pattern was for the man, after marriage, to reside with his wife's family; being a non-relative, he was thus an outsider until he in turn had children and grandchildren. His own parental home was a rallying place when any relative became ill, or any danger or sorrow threatened. At other times, visits were looked upon with displeasure since there was no longer any place for him to sleep, and the food he ate was not of his earning, but now belonged entirely to the others.

Young Boy said, "Grandfather, I must go outside."

"Come," said Deerhunter, "we shall go together." An older person always accompaned a youngster when he had to take care of nature's needs, in order to instruct the child in the proper method of hiding all traces.

Deerhunter and Young Boy left the sweathouse and walked some distance into the brush, careful not to make any noise, peering in every direction, wary of being seen. When Deerhunter was satisfied that no one was about, he dug a small hole for Young Boy.

The western slopes across the valley were clearly visible in the moonlight, and portions of the valley floor could be seen emerging from what but days ago had been the swirling waters of the annual flood. With the passing of the rains the valley eventually drained, the land became firm, and the gummy mud that made hunting or traveling so difficult disappeared. It had been a long hard winter, and the early snows on the surrounding mountains had lasted longer than they had for many years. If another snow or rain should come upon them, the unusually severe winter would bring hardship; both the food supply and the people's tempers were short. "I shall have to talk to the Yomta again about the Ceremony," thought Deerhunter.

In the stillness, the old man kept watch, the cold and dampness penetrating his flesh. When Young Boy stood erect the feces were carefully covered so that no enemy could find them and use them for poisoning. After camouflaging the area they returned to the sweathouse by a circuitous route.

The old man looked up at the heavens and noticed that the crescent moon was in a horizontal position with the horns upward. He said exultantly, "That is good—it means that we shall not have any more rain! If the moon were in the vertical position, the water would spill out, and we would have another month of rain and winter weather."

"I shall be glad when summer comes," said Young Boy. "I am tired of the rain and mud."

When they returned to the sweathouse, Deerhunter was cold, and the fire had been allowed to die down in his absence. He stirred the embers briskly before adding wood. His face was lit sharply as the flames flickered and danced. The ceiling, which had seemed dim and distant through the slowly undulating cloud of smoke, was visible for a moment; the old charred peeled logs of the roof looked strong enough to withstand an avalanche.

In the new brightness, he could see Man of Many Beads in a cluster of laughing and talking young men. Man of Many Beads was a young man of considerable status and prestige since he belonged to a large and important family and was also a skilled deer hunter and gambler. He shifted his six feet of lean, muscular, tawny body upon the twined rabbit skin blanket. He was a handsome representative of the men of his age group. His smooth muscles rippled as he settled his broad shoulders and narrow hips; his face was attractively virile with wide-spaced dark brown eyes, small ears set close to his head, a straight nose, and good bone structure with moderately high cheekbones.

Although he joined in the merriment of the group, he was thinking of what his wife, Long Haired Woman, had said earlier as she had given him dinner about the lingering winter and the alarmingly low level of the food in the storage baskets. Tonight it had barely been sufficient to stay his appetite. He only half-listened as Wakim went on with his stories. "Another time Foolish Man was out with the others on a hunting trip to get gray squirrels. As all the men were beating around and closing in on the small creatures, some in the trees and some on the ground, somebody shouted, 'There he goes; hit him; hit him with a stick.' The men in high spirits all gave chase, yelling and hollering, Foolish Man in the rear. A gray squirrel leapt towards him. The others cried out, 'Foolish Man, he is going in your direction; hit him, hit him.'

"But Foolish Man just stood still and talked to the squirrel,

'Go on, go on, have courage, my friend. I don't know why they want to kill you; you are beautiful. You have done no one any harm. So have courage and go on, go on, my friend.'

"One of the older men was so angry at this behavior that he threw an arrow at Foolish Man."

The listeners laughed.

An older man said, "Yes, he is an odd one. Once he came all the way from Clear Lake with a load of fish. As is customary, some of the poor old people paid him a visit, as they do when anyone comes in with a good catch, expecting a handout. Foolish Man had just laid down his loaded basket when an old woman came into his house and sat down very close to him. He paid no attention to her. To each of several others who came in later, he gave one or two fish even before they sat down. When the visitors ceased coming, the old woman got up and left empty-handed.

"Foolish Man's wife said to him, 'You have done a bad thing. What made you act like that? That old woman is terribly offended at the way you treated her.'

"He answered brusquely. 'She made me angry because she came in too soon and sat down too close to me.'"

The listeners laughed uproariously.

Now the fire was bright, and it was pleasantly warm. The smoke that floated at shoulder height was not disturbing to those sitting or lying down. The conversations rambled pleasantly and idly from subject to subject with only occasional emphasis upon matters of importance.

In one area four deer hunters were continuing their ritualistic preparations of dances, prayers, and ceremonies as they had been doing for the three previous days. They kept apart from the other individuals in the sweathouse because they were "fixed" for hunting and were being especially careful not to touch or be touched by anyone.

Another group consisted of fishermen talking over the prospects now that the flood had subsided and it would be possible to set traps in the pools that had been left.

Despite the comradeship of the sweathouse Man of Many Beads felt lonely because his *awihinawa* was absent. His *awihinawa* was confined to his wife's cubicle because if her month-sickness; a man whose wife was in that condition remained at home not only to care for her but also because during her period it was taboo for him to participate in any usual activity, like hunting or gambling. Two men who were *awihinawa* were constant companions, and when something happened to separate them, each felt inadequate. An *awihinawa* was the only person of one's age grade upon whom one could rely. Closer than a brother, he was the one person who was counted on to protect you in combat even at the cost of his own life; if you were wounded he got between you and the enemy, or carried you off the field. He was the go-between in making dates with girls. There were even times when two *awihinawa* had one girl between them.

As a young boy he had played with other boys of his age grade, but as time passed he had spent increasingly more time with the one boy who bore the same name as his own. Each family had made certain that the other boy was not a member of an enemy family. At approximately fourteen years of age, he and his friend were made members of each others' families in a small public ceremony and were called by the same relationship terms in each family. This was the beginning of a life-long association which ended only with the death of one or both parties; however, the relationship between families continued.

Awihinawa was most important and almost universal between two men but was less frequent between two women.

There were only a few men who did not have an *awihinawa*. Those who dressed like women and lived like women, some even in a married relationship to another man, did not have that tie. When a man was left alone at the death of his *awihinawa*, he could not acquire another, since the relationship had to be established at an early age. For a man to be without an *awihinawa* was unfortunate; in this culture, where insecurity was all-pervasive, the backing of an additional family was a great asset, but most important was the existence of an individual in whom one could freely confide one's hopes, fears, and ambitions.

Wakim, sitting beside Man of Many Beads, was his *awihinawa's* younger brother; so Wakim was like a younger brother to him in every respect except that the brothers were not in the same marital grouping. Neither *awihinawa* nor his brother would take over Long Haired Woman and the children in the event of Man of Many Beads' death; only a biological brother could do so.

Man of Many Beads moved closer to Wakim who was sitting beside his own *awihinawa* and asked after his brother.

"He is still at his wife's home—I saw him through the doorway as I came up here," said Wakim. He lowered his voice, "He is not as fortunate as I, who will soon be with a woman if no one interferes."

Many of Many Beads chuckled as he said, "You must be careful or you will soon be sitting in your own wife's home waiting for her to have your son."

Wakim laughed, looked meaningfully at his *awihinawa*, and said, "It is almost time for me to leave."

His *awihinawa* said, "Come back soon."

All three understood that should Wakim be followed out of the sweathouse by any relative of the girl with whom he had a rendezvous, his *awihinawa* would follow to warn him with a pre-arranged signal.

The exchange reminded Man of Many Beads of his own experience the day before. He had gone into the eastern foothills to ascertain the area in which the deer were feeding. Although the deer were undomesticated they were utilized like farm herds. The deer hunters knew the size and composition of the different herds, were careful to kill only the surplus bucks, and thinned the herds when they appeared to be overly large for the available grazing. They knew that if the grazing became insufficient the deer would wander out of the valley seeking food and thus be lost to them.

On the trail coming home in the afternoon he had met his brother's wife's sister. Joking about sex between two people who stood in that relationship was not only permissible but expected. Before they knew what had happened they had mated. She was the only woman with whom he had been intimate since his marriage, and he felt that it would not have happened but that Long Haired Woman had shown little interest in sex for some time.

31

At a moment when he thought he would be least noticed Wakim strolled out of the sweathouse. He had been meeting Kabemok secretly for some time and looked forward to seeing her again. It was now four days since they had been together; she had become month-sick, for which both had been relieved and happy. The first night she was in the menstrual hut, a small thatched enclosure connected to her family house, where the unmarried women of the family had to remain during their periods, his desire had been so great that he had visited her surreptitiously, even though menstrual blood was considered the most dangerous thing with which a man could come in contact.

The first time, some months ago, when Wakim had been with Kabemok during her isolation, he had fearfully expected retaliation from the supernaturals, and had immediately taken a cold bath in the river to decontaminate himself. But he had been less fearful of late, and not for more than a day or two.

He thought with reminiscent dismay how close he had come to making a blunder on the second night, when he had learned only just in time that two other girls of the family had also been placed in the menstrual hut. A tremor of fear passed through him as he thought of the possible consequences.

Wakim waited quietly near the trysting place in the brush outside the village. It was a cold night, yet he was warm with anticipation. He could hear the night sounds of the village in the distance; close at hand he heard the sounds of birds nestling in the underbrush.

His eagerness made him impatient. Perhaps Kabemok had not been able to get away from the house tonight. That had happened before. He wished it weren't necessary to hurry the tryst so much, but if Kabemok were to be away more than the few minutes necessary to take care of nature's needs, suspicion would be aroused and female relatives would come searching for her.

He heard a rustle different from the sound of leaves or small animals moving towards him. Only a few whispered words passed between them, and there were few preliminaries before their two bodies were intermingled in a passionate embrace.

"Tomorrow night?" asked Wakim, when they were done. Kabemok leaned close to whisper her assent. She straightened her clothes, brushed off the grass and leaves, while Wakim moved away through the night. She gave him sufficient time to get far enough away so that when she entered the house, if her delay did rouse suspicion, he would not be overtaken and identified.

Wakim moved off through the brush in a state of combined elation and anxiety. If Kabemok were to become pregnant, and the two families should find out that he was responsible, he would have to marry her. Refusal was out of the question and would be considered unfriendly to the point of enmity and arouse suspicion of a family attempt at "poisoning." If he got married, however, he could have this woman without all of the furtiveness and worry. But then he couldn't have other women without the worry of Kabemok's finding out. Now he could have as many as he could get. However, he realized that he was no longer interested in any other woman.

During the past autumn, when all the people were gathering acorns, picking berries, gathering grass seed, and in general roaming over the hills, it had been pleasanter. They had had more time together, and were not missed when they strayed. It had been easy for Kabemok to say she had been with different relatives, or else Wakim had helped her pick many berries so she would have something material to show for her absence. It had been good to find some thick brush and sit and talk and make love. He remembered how frightened she was when they had been together for the first time, how she had whimpered when it was over. As every virgin was supposed to do, she had scratched his face; he had then to concoct a story of having fallen into thorny bushes. But the men, as was also customary, had joked about his scratched face. He had been proud, yet at the same time had resented the joking. He had had difficulty persuading her to be with him the next few times, but at last she left off resisting, and they came together regularly. Compared with the ease of their lovemaking in the fall, the present arrangement was troublesome and disappointing.

As Kabemok walked back towards her house, she too thought about the possibilities of becoming pregnant. Then she decided not to worry because there were ways of taking care of that. She knew about the use of mistletoe, having overheard her married

33

female relatives talking about it one day when they were unaware of her presence. They had agreed that it was a revolting-tasting brew, but some of them had been drinking the juice of half a small basketful every month in order not to become pregnant. There were prayers, incantations, and songs, too, that she would have to learn. She wondered how, as an unmarried girl, she would go about solving these difficulties, even if she learned all the rituals and procedures. How could she brew the mistletoe without her relatives' knowledge? Perhaps her older sister would do it for her. Then she wondered whether she ought not to get pregnant so that she and Wakim could get married.

Wakim returned to the sweathouse, sat down again between his *awihinawa* and Man of Many Beads, and entered easily into the conversations.

Deerhunter was talking to the Yomta, who was the head religious man of the valley, about the persistent winter.

"I have started preparations for the ceremony," the Yomta told him. During the greater part of the year his status was very much like that of every other man, but during the periodical religious ceremonies he was the seat of power and authority, a man of utmost importance. It was his role to direct the formal religion just as it was for the war chief to administer wars and raids, for the oldest deer hunter to assume power in communal deer hunts, and for the head fisherman to be the leader in the communal fishing parties. At all other times, the Head Man of each family, together with the Head Woman of that family, was the seat of all authority and power in each family.

Some of the Head Men had been discussing the most important religious ceremony, held annually in different valleys and every seventh year in Yokiah Valley, since it was centrally located and heavily populated. Tribes from Shanel to the south and Upper Lake to the west also participated in the seven year cycle. Other smaller tribes were hosts less frequently, depending on available food supply, objects of trade, the death of a Chief, intertribal difficulties, and the approval by the Yomta.

From the way in which these revered and powerful men had

been conferring, it was clear that public opinion had been formed and that the proper time for action had arrived. Earlier the talk about the long winter and the overdue dry weather had obliged the Yomta to begin preparations for the lesser ceremony that was preliminary to any Big-Time—in this case the ceremony that heralded the end of the rains.

When he was certain that all of the Head Men of the important families were in agreement concerning the temper of the people, the Yomta discussed the matter with the Chief and then approached a male relative who had been born during the summer months, when no rain ever fell, and said to him, "The rains have continued too long and the food supply is getting dangerously low. There is much talk about preparing for the important religious Big-Time, in which we cannot participate as long as we still have wet weather. It is time for me to perform the ceremony to bring on dry weather, and in order to do that properly I will need eight hairs from your head."

Under ordinary circumstances no individual would allow his hair, his nail parings, or any other part of his body to get into the hands of any other person, except a blood relative, for fear that it would be used to poison him. But because of the blood relationship, the importance of bringing dry weather, and the fact that the Yomta was a trusted religious man, the man cooperated willingly.

The Yomta, accompanied by his older assistants, who had already achieved religious status, and by the younger men who were in training, with no further delay ushered the chosen man to a special place in the foothills where the brush was dense; there he ceremonially took eight hairs from his head while he and his assistants prayed and chanted to the supernaturals.

When this preliminary ritual was done, he directed the gathering of the prescribed roots, flowers, and plants, each of which was related to the dry weather months. All was then in readiness for the main ceremony the next day.

It had grown late. In the sweathouse the men were preparing for the night. Some of the older ones stretched out on their rabbit-skin blankets, their young grandsons close beside them.

A few of the young married men were preparing to return home. Some had already left surreptitiously, to escape the inevitable joking about their young wives.

During the night, one or another old man, awakened by the cold, would poke the embers and place some wood upon the fire. Again the flames would lick and flare. The sweathouse never became completely quiet. There was at all times a low murmur of voices, for everyone had been trained to make some noise on waking so that any enemy group who might approach the settlement would think the people awake and alert. Similar sounds of stirring and talk came from houses all over the village.

As dawn approached the men fed the fire until it flamed and roared. One by one the sleepers threw off their robes, stretched, sat up, and resumed talk. In a little while their naked bodes glistened with steaming sweat, and the atmosphere became stifling. The men used fans to send the heat away from themselves toward those on the opposite side of the fire. They called back and forth good-naturedly to one another. "Eh, you old woman, how do you like to eat fire?"

"You there, I'm cold, blow some fire my way."

Some of the men had green tule in their mouths to help them withstand the heat.

When the heat became unbearable, they made a concerted rush towards the door and plunged for their morning bath into the icy stream, where they splashed and splattered. Then they returned to the sweathouse, which by that time had cooled to a comfortable temperature.

They then performed their morning toilets, arranging their nose and ear plugs and coiffures.

In the daylight and the light of the blazing fire, the sweathouse was revealed as a semi-subterranean structure, the floor of which was a few feet below ground. Logs and poles made up the roof, which was covered with branches, grass, and soil; from the outside it looked like a large mound of earth.

Soon all the men scattered to their homes for breakfast.

At the appointed time the men who were to assist the Yomta arrived at the Round-House, where while praying and chanting, they dressed in their ceremonial costumes. Then they built a small fire, and all chanted the prayers as the Yomta placed the ritual ingredients into the flames. As was standard for all ceremonies, they prayed to the six directions, to the four points of the compass, to the sky above and the earth below. The Yomta then held his hands out over the fire, and the ceremony was completed with additional prayers, during which the men took off their costumes and put them away. Then they disbanded.

Before the Yomta entered his home, he carefully performed the ceremony which broke all relationships with the Universe and the Supernaturals with whom he had been in contact. Every participant in the ceremony had to do the same; if he did not, the occupants of his house, especially the young children and pregnant women, would be in danger of immediate sickness and death.

The Yomta hung his sacred bundle up near the inner roof so that its shadow would not fall upon any member of the household, then turned and left the house, walking slowly in the direction of the sweathouse. He was tired; every ceremony he performed was enervating, for one mistake on his part, be it an omission or change of arrangement or sequence, would bring severe hardship and even death to the population. For four days before any ceremony he was obliged to abstain from all meat, fish, and fats. In fact he was permitted to eat only a small amount of pinole, a pulverized cereal. Now that his fast was over, he wanted to relax for a little while before going back to his home for a hearty meal.

Chapter II

AFTER their evening meal, Man of Many Beads' wife said:
"Come here, and I shall clean your face and trim your eyebrows. It doesn't look well for my husband to go to the men's house with his face untended."

Man of Many Beads knelt before her readily for this customary grooming.

Long Haired Woman scraped her husband's beard with the obsidian flake until his skin was smooth, then carefully plucked his eyebrows with the clamshell tweezers.

"There." She surveyed her work intently. "Now you may go."

Her husband thanked her and went out. The stars were so thickly strewn that it seemed necessary to bend his head to avoid dislodging them. The brilliant moon illuminated the entire valley; he could see its reflection in the river. There was a murmur and rumble of voices coming from the many dwellings and the sounds of movements into and from the bush. When he came into the light of the fire in the sweathouse, a few of the older men glanced in his direction and began to chuckle. At the sound, others turned to look, and soon a number were howling with mirth.

Man of Many Beads was disconcerted, for he realized that he was the cause of the merriment. After some of the hilarity had subsided an old man indicated the cause of it. "She knows you were with another woman."

Slowly, Man of Many Beads raised his hand to his eyebrows. They were as smooth as the rest of his face. Long Haired

Woman had not only removed the superfluous hair from his face, but had plucked his eyebrows clean, this being a means of shaming and punishing an errant husband.

Another old man, a relative of Man of Many Beads, said, "You are lucky—not like Strong Woman's husband. She caught him all naked rutting a woman and jumped on him and pulled his penis out of joint. He died in a few days."

An old woman coughed for attention. "You talk about what women do to men," she said. "How about what men do to women? There have been cases of a man's biting off his wife's nose to make her ugly so that other men would not look at her. And that's happened even when she had done no wrong, only spoken to another man or given him a drink of water. And sometimes men have stuck pointed sticks or sting rays into their wives' eyes to blind them so they would have to stay at home. And you all know of husbands having killed their wives with a spear."

Man of Many Beads turned away from this discussion to join the younger men. He squatted beside them, attempting by his demeanor to convey the impression that nothing out of the ordinary had occurred.

"Such harsh deeds are the ways of our people," said one old man, resignedly. "A mate who discovers that the spouse has had sexual relations with another can do such things. If no one else knows the matter can be ignored, but if one does nothing when everyone knows what has happened, one is considered a nobody and is laughed at. I for one do not believe that there should be killing for these reasons. Man is man and woman is woman, and all have the same urges. Nothing is lost, and no one is hurt. Coyote always does it, and he made the world, he made men—he made everything. We all know the tales in which Coyote tricks and then ruts Thunder's wife. Doesn't he trick everyone, including young girls and married women whom he meets casually in the fields or whom he sometimes causes to meet him in the brush? Why, he even tricks and then ruts his own mother-in-law, and we all know that that's the worst thing!"

Another old man spoke up. "Yes, that is true about Coyote, but we can't do everything he does and we shouldn't try to. If everyone acted that way, there would soon be no family left. Men would not know their own children and women could not take care of the children by themselves. And we old men would have no children or grandchildren of our own to take care of us. Who would feed us? Who would cremate us properly? No, it's better for a husband and wife to stay together. After all, a married man can be with his wife's relatives without causing trouble. He does not have to find strange women, whose families might only be trying to poison him."

By this time it was clear that every aspect of the subject would be thoroughly reviewed for the benefit of all those present. For one thing, old people acquired prestige when they recounted some folklore, myth, example, or historical case, but the main purpose of such discussion was to impress the young men with the modes of the culture.

Poisoning did not apply to members within the tribe, but rather to members of other tribes doing it to the members of the Yokiah tribe. It was never admitted or even insinuated, publicly, that poisoning went on among members of the same tribe. The mere admission of knowledge of poisoning was tantamount to a confession that the individual was participating in the poisoning of others; any family with a sick member would immediately institute countermeasures against the suspect and every member of his family.

The same was true of gossip. One never gossiped about a non-family member nor complained about him, for to do so would be an admission, and in some cases a boast, that one was in the process of poisoning him or his family. The suspicion of poisoning and the care taken to avoid it was extreme; any object offered to an individual was taken with the left hand and transferred to the right, the receiver meanwhile silently praying to the supernaturals; this was believed to draw out the poison from the object. If members of the family were present the object was always handed initially to the oldest male; any other procedure was suspect. The oldest male then passed it to the next oldest male, and so on. In that way all potential danger was removed by the powerful ones before it got into the hands of the women and children.

The old man continued, "We would destroy our ways of life if we did not punish one another for wrongdoing and thus prevent others from doing the same.

"If a man were to participate as Coyote has he would be in trouble as often; and we must remember what troubles Coyote's tricks led to—destruction of the world and of our ancestors!"

"Yes, I feel as you do," an old woman chimed in. "It would be far better if wives and husbands stayed at home together. But we are old and have forgotten what youth is like. Just the same, violence always does harm and never good. A lot of trouble started in just this way; and today there are many families that out of anger killed off all but a few of their members, and they're poor and cannot take care of themselves if they get sick. It is bad enough to have troubles from other causes; we are always afraid that we have done something wrong and sometimes we forget to take care of the supernaturals. Then we get sick and must call in the doctor."

Another old man had his say. "When two young people are married there is little reason for them to seek out others. But our customs are such that sometimes a man's old relative dies, and he finds himself married to a woman old enough to be his grandmother. When that happens you cannot blame him for taking a young woman. But, that is another question. There are many reasons why it is dangerous for men to be with strange women. Some of our hunters and travelers who go to out-of-the-way and lonely places have met with the Da-mata, the Sun-girls, who live near water, and who are very beautiful. These women entice the men to sexual intercourse, which kills them, because the Sun-girls' vaginas contain live rattlesnakes."

"It is not only the Sun-girls," the old man went on, his sonorous voice carrying to every corner of the sweathouse, "but any woman of another tribe, who might be trying to poison you. She may act as if she is very passionate and a virgin, and when she scratches you with her nails as virgins must do, she may have some poison concealed under them. There is the story of Morning-Star, whose two daughters lived in a house quite a distance away. They were unable to find husbands because Morning-Star was jealous of all the young men and watched his daughters so very closely that no one ventured to court them.

42

At last Wood Rat dared go to the house. He tried for a long time to get one of the sisters to marry him. At last the elder sister said, 'All right, I will marry you, but you must know that my father has placed thorns all about my vagina.'

"Rat then took a stone and broke off all the thorns and married the girl. But if he hadn't been warned he would have been killed." He shook his head. "Yes, sex can be very dangerous," he added.

Fleetingly there passed through Wakim's mind fearful thoughts about Kabemok. But she loved him, he knew; she would never harm him. It was her relatives who might be dangerous. There were no thorns or rattlesnakes in Kabemok, no more than there had been in any other woman he'd been with. He relaxed. "These are only old people's myths," he thought. Then he became afraid again, this time that the supernaturals would punish him.

He consciously made himself listen to another old man who was saying, "There is another story which fits in with what we are discussing. After Obsidian Man, with the help of his father, Coyote, had performed some marvelous feats in order to obtain a wife, one of the three remaining Thunder Brothers, acknowledging him as his son-in-law, showed him where his daughter's bed was located. Obsidian Man told his father about Thunder's directions, and Coyote, at once suspicious, replied, 'I will fix that. I will go there first. He is trying to trick us again!'

"As soon as Coyote came near Thunder Man's daughter, rattlesnakes tried to bite him, but he had a weed with which to kill them. The bride had many snakes twined all over her body so that anyone who came near her would be killed. Coyote killed all the rattlesnakes, after which it was safe for Obsidian Man to go to Thunder Man's daughter."

The younger men had listened attentively to the talk. They all knew that it was essentially a means of impressing them with the importance of the means of control, the dangers involved in everyday life, and the fact that it was stupid to look for trouble when there was always more than enough already lying in wait for everyone. Direct censure was seldom applied, but when it was, it was most severe.

Man of Many Beads felt like speaking up, but knew that

43

anything he said would invite more joking and laughter and would diminish his status. He remained quiet although he was angry and ashamed. Yet he knew he was in the wrong and that in fact he had got off rather easily because of the joking relationship he had with the other woman, a relationship which every member of the tribe had with certain categories of relatives, who, under certain circumstances, could marry each other. Other categories of individuals were taboo. However, the joking relationship did not automatically allow sexual intercourse. If it occurred between two unmarried individuals and became known, it usually led to marriage.

When one of the two parties was married, the act was unpunished by anyone but the spouse since one did not initiate intrafamilial trouble; usually the unfaithful spouse was punished in a comparatively mild fashion as Man of Many Beads had been. But when a married person had illicit sexual intercourse with a member of another family or a relative who was taboo, the spouse imposed severe punishment, especially if the couple had children. There were a number of reasons for this, the most important of which was the possibility of poisoning of both the individual and the entire family. Jealousy, too, was present.

"I'm glad it wasn't Long Haired Woman who actually saw us," Man of Many Beads thought. "There would have been greater trouble. I wonder who did see us."

It was so difficult to do anything secretly. There were always people in the bush, taking care of nature's needs, or having their own clandestine meetings, or hunting, or engaging in religious ceremonies, and they were always so quiet that one would hardly realize they were nearby.

He had a strong impulse to leave the sweathouse in order to talk with his *awihinawa*, who would be sympathetic and to whom he could air his troubles, but he could not leave without injuring his prestige and his reputation for courage. The men would know they had disconcerted and shamed him, and he felt obliged to remain and act nonchalant.

He thought uneasily of his notoriety; his entire family would soon know about the situation if they did not know about it already. He anticipated, with no pleasure, the censure he would receive, especially from the women of his family who would be

44

angry with him—and for good reason. He could also anticipate the combination of smirking and censure he would get from his male relatives; the implication would be that he had been careless and less of a man than they had thought because he had been found out.

Smoke from the fire smarted his eyes, and he rubbed them, his attention returning again to the still-talking old people.

"On the other hand," an old woman was saying, "women too must be on their guard at all times. A man may be trying to poison her, or some especially attractive man may really be Coyote in disguise. There is the story of Coyote's seeing two young women gathering buckeye and changing himself into an old woman, a tired old woman carrying a basket, who said to the girls, 'It looks like rain. I am going to make a lean-to, and we can all sleep here and keep dry.'

"She made a shelter just large enough for the three, then slipped away and ordered a very hard rain to begin. Soon, indeed, it began to pour.

"The three entered the shelter, the old woman between the two young ones, and they all went to sleep. The old woman then changed herself into a young man, who said, 'I wish them to sleep very soundly.' They did, whereupon he rutted both of them.

"When the girls awoke they each had two children. When they came toward camp with them, the other women came out yelling and screaming and killed the children."

"That's true," the old man said. "A woman can never tell when she meets a young man or an old woman whether or not it's really Coyote. A woman who mates with Coyote always has two or four or more children, and these children of Coyote's are always treated very badly by the people. Sometimes they are all killed, sometimes only two are left, and sometimes two pairs of twins are left. There is always trouble about twins because of Coyote. They must be killed immediately; if the children are allowed to live as many as three days after birth, it is too late. After that if you punish them at any time or if you do not feed them well, there is always trouble. In the past Coyote has burned up the world and destroyed the people for that very reason."

45

"I agree with much of what has been said," said another old man. "If we don't refrain from acts that cause trouble and don't punish each other, who will make us act right? We would all get mean and ugly-tempered, and then there would be continuous growling and fighting. We would get careless and forget the supernaturals, and then the entire tribe would suffer."

A very old man, his face wrinkled and dark from his many years, his eyes bloodshot and half-closed from the smoke of many fires, raised his head. "Yes, all that's been said here is true. Everyone must be careful of his dreams, his thoughts, and his actions, for the threat of danger is constant."

Chapter III

THE young boys, their attention wandering, moved about from one group to another. A few lay stretched out alongside their grandfathers in quiet and intimate conversation.

The old man seated himself next to the Yomta. "The moon is bright tonight, the air is cool, and there is a light wind from the east. It should be dry soon."

"That would be good," said the Yomta.

Another Head Man said, "Soon it will get warm and pleasant for traveling. It will be easier for people to travel long distances for a Big-Time."

The Yomta understood from these remarks that the pressure for formal action was becoming sufficiently intense for him to start active preparations. It was time to see the Chief about calling a Council meeting. Yes—perhaps a few more days. He would have to sound out each Head Man separately.

There was always a period of gathering of public opinion before any activity involving the total tribal group was undertaken. The time depended upon a considerable number of factors. Someone might suggest the possibility of action to an old friend who also was the Head Man of a family. If there were agreement, the matter would be cautiously brought to the attention of another Head Man, and then another, until it was felt that they were all in agreement, at which time the matter would be brought to the attention of whatever leader was involved, who in his turn brought it to the notice of the Chief. The process was always carried on cautiously and by indirection; the few

47

exceptions had created trouble. Unanimity of group opinion was required before formal action was instituted. If at any time opposition became apparent, the entire matter was usually dropped.

The Yomta knew that soon again he would be denying himself many pleasures because of the rigorous taboos and necessary preparations for the important religious Big-Time that came at the end of the bitter winter season.

On the other side of the fire, the old man motioned his grandson over to him and said, "You have heard much tonight. You are getting old enough to know more about important things. Tonight you have heard of the dangers that result from intimacies with the wrong woman. But that is only one of many possible troubles; for we live in an environment fraught with terrible dangers. Not only people, but the supernaturals, the rocks, the waters, the trees, the animals, in fact everything about us has power to harm us. We must be careful always. We can only find relief from anxiety with our own blood relatives and our *awihinawas*. Even your wife and the members of her family are dangerous because sometimes marriage is arranged so that one family can get control of another."

The boy stirred uneasily. "Grandfather, why is it that we must be careful if a woman is month-sick? Why is she so dangerous to us?"

"When a woman is month-sick she is taboo. You must abide by the taboos, or you will lose all your money when you gamble, you will fail in your hunts, you will become very sick, and you may die. Even if the doctors cure you, you will still be in danger because the cure will have been so costly and you will have little wealth to take care of another sickness in your family. You must always be sure to be on guard against contamination from menstruating women. Do not allow them near you. Stay away from them—they are dangerous."

"But, Grandfather, how can you know when a woman is month-sick? There are always old women in the sweathouse with us."

"These women are different. When they get old, they no longer have month-sickness. Now they are like men, and are no longer dangerous. Menstrual blood is one of the most nega-

48

tive forces, and women too must be very careful. They know that if they go about while they are menstruating, they may meet monsters who will make them sick and cause their deaths; that is why they stay in the house. If they are away from home and happen to get month-sick, they must say certain prayers and be especially careful. You don't have to worry about your own relatives because when they are month-sick, they go to the menstrual house and take care of things properly. You can always rely upon your blood relatives for aid and protection. You must be good to them; you must not growl at them; you must give them presents and help them at all times; but even with them you must be careful because they can unwittingly cause you a great deal of harm by breaking a taboo or getting involved in a feud."

Young Boy lost interest. He said, "You've told me these things so many times, Grandfather."

"I have indeed." There was a slight rebuke in Grandfather's voice. "And I shall repeat everything I have said, again and again, for that is the only way in which they'll become a part of you and help to keep you out of trouble.

"When a feud begins, remember that you and every member of the family are fair game for enemies. To combat the enemy's poison, you must all be constantly on guard, for once a member is sick, every enemy will then try to add poison, because when a sick person is weak, every member of the family is involved with the supernaturals, who are divided into two groups; at such times they are especially vulnerable and may be easily killed.

"Only your blood relatives comprise your sanctuary, and you can rely only on them. The times you're with them are the only ones when you can relax from your constant vigilance. It's your family members who will take care of you when you are young and when you are old, when you are sick, when you are hungry, and when you are in need of money. But even when you are close to home or in it, you must be careful. Each older man, as you know, hangs his bundle, which contains all his power for his profession, close to the roof. If a bundle becomes too powerful its very shadow will kill a child, and it will also make it impossible for a woman to become pregnant. So with members

49

of your own family, as well as other valley families, you must be careful at all times. And now it is time to say something about your own tribal group."

The young boy's interest perked up, but his attention soon wandered again as the old man droned on.

"Our people in this valley act as a cooperative, unified group during the communal fishing, rabbit, quail, and deer drives, for at those times every family and each individual benefits. That's true too in the case of aggression from an outside group, as for example when members of an outside tribe trespass on our land. There is a ceremony, as you know, before the warriors start out, and the whole population supports them. All thoughts and fears of feuds and poisoning and other such troubles are set aside. This is also true during a shortage of food, when everyone helps everyone else. During a severe shortage the Council selects our strongest men and women to make a hurried trip to the coast to bring back all kinds of food from the sea, which is then distributed among our families as needed.

"You can also rely on our tribal group during the formal wars although there have been very few of them in our history. Then the entire tribal group again acts as a unit, with no reference to internal conflicts."

"Is it only in time of war, Grandfather, that another group is our enemy?" the boy asked.

"No, my grandson, every other group at all times is considered a potential enemy of our people. Even when we visit them for religious ceremonies or for trading purposes, we are still very careful because that is the best time for poisoning. It's especially at those times that you must watch everyone, even members of your own tribal group. The farther you go from your own home and your own blood relatives, the more the danger increases. And when you get into the mountains you will find not only potential enemies, but many supernatural creatures. That's one of the reasons a young person like you doesn't go alone, but with an older person who knows the proper procedures and has power. You can protect yourself against the supernaturals by prayer and offerings—as you grow older you will learn more about all that. But there are times when it is almost impossible to take care of them all. Your wife, for instance, may become month-sick while you are on a hunting trip. I remember once when I was deer hunting and saw a spotted deer. I shot all of my arrows and yet, experienced a hunter as I am, didn't hit the creature. Then I realized there was something wrong, although I had danced, prayed, and made my offerings in preparation for my trip. I had refrained from eating meat, grease, and the other things for four days, and had cleansed myself properly. It was only when I returned home that I found that my wife had become month-sick.

"There are many supernaturals. Even though we are familiar with the ones in our own territory, when things go wrong they may take your life.

"And the farther you go from our valley the less you know about the supernaturals, and the more dangerous they become. So you see that the greatest safety is in your own valley with your own family, and the larger and richer the family you have, the more professionals in it, the greater the safety."

By this time Grandson's head was nodding, and he was struggling to keep his eyes open.

Chapter IV

THE curiosity of another youngster, Little Boy, had been stimulated by the conversation. He asked his grandfather, "Where do those dangerous Sun-girls live?"

The old man looked thoughtfully at the eager, questioning boy. "Ai," he said, "to explain that thoroughly I would have to tell you a great deal about the universe. It is a long story—about where we come from—about the birds, the animals, the waters, the mountains, and a lot more. Aren't you too tired to hear such a long story tonight?"

"Oh, no, Grandfather!" exclaimed the boy. "I'd like to hear all about it."

The grandfather settled himself comfortably, and leaned on one elbow, for, as he knew, to sit erect while recounting religious history made one hunchbacked. He started from the beginning. "In early times nothing was as you see it now. Coyote was let down from the zenith by Spider after he had created both of the upper worlds. In his hunting sack he carried the sun, moon, clouds, water, and a small bit of earth. He, this Marumda, looked about and saw nothing but water. He then told Spider to spin some more web. Then he spread the earth upon the web, and that is how the land was made."

Wakim, who was lying nearby thinking of Kabemok, listened to the old man and realized that the presentation of the introduction had been telescoped. Sometimes an old man went into great length about the creation of the earth and the universe, sometimes the stress was placed upon the creation of man, sometimes on other aspects, depending on what lessons the old man wanted to emphasize for his audience.

"He lived in the north," continued the grandfather. "The Old Man's name was Marumda. He lived in a cloud-house, a house that looked like snow, like ice. And he thought of making the world. 'I will ask my older brother who lives in the south,' thus he said, the Old Man Marumda . . ."

The old man was using the religious and ceremonial language required for the recounting of the religious history.

"Four times he lay down to sleep, and then he floated to his elder brother's house. His name was Kuksu, Kuksu, the elder brother of Marumda.

"The Kuksu, his house was like a cloud, like snow, like ice. Around it floated the four hairs which Marumda had plucked from his own head, four times they floated around it, and then through a hole they floated into the house, and following them the Marumda entered the house . . .

"He took out his pipe and filled it with tobacco, he laid a coal on it, and he blew, he blew, and then he blew it afire. Then he removed the coal and put it back into his little sack. After that he smoked, four times he put the pipe to his mouth. After that he offered it to his older brother the Kuksu . . .

"And then the Marumda scraped himself in the armpits, he scraped himself and got out some of the armpit wax. He gave the armpit wax to the Kuksu. Then Kuksu received it, he received it, and stuck it in between his big toe and the next. And then he also scraped himself in the armpits, he scraped himself, and rolled the armpit wax into a ball. His own armpit wax he then stuck between Marumda's toes.

"Then Marumda removed it and blew on it, four times he blew on it. Then Kuksu also removed the armpit wax and blew on it four times, and after that he sat down. Then Marumda went around the Kuksu four times, and then he sat down. And then the Kuksu he got up, he got up, and four times around the Marumda he went. Then they both stood still.

"Now they mixed together their balls of armpit wax. And Kuksu mixed some of his hair with the armpit wax.

"After they stood up, facing south, and then facing east, and

54

then facing north, and then facing west, and then facing the zenith, and then facing the nadir: 'These words are to be right and thus everything will be. People are going to be according to this plan. There is going to be food according to this plan. There will be food from the water! There will be food from the land. There will be food from under the ground. There will be food from the air. There will be all kinds of food whereby the people will be healthy. These people will have good intentions. Their villages will be good. They will plan many things. They will be full of knowledge. There will be many of them on this earth, and their intentions will be good.

" 'We are going to make in the sky the traveling-fire. With it they will ripen their food. We are going to make that with which they will cook their food overnight. The traveling-fires in the sky, their name will be the Sun. The one who is Fire, his name will be Daytime-Sun. The one who gives light in the night, her name will be Night-Sun. These words are right. This plan is sound. Everything according to this plan is going to be right!' Thus he spoke, the Kuksu.

"And now the Marumda made a speech. Holding the armpit wax, holding it to the south, he made a wish: 'These words are right!' Thus he said, the Marumda. And then he held it to the east, and then he held it to the north, and then he held it to the west, and then he held it to the zenith, and then he held it to the nadir: 'According to this plan, people are going to be. There are going to be people on this earth. On this earth there will be plenty of food for the people! According to this plan there will be many different kinds of food for the people! Clover in plenty will grow. Grain, acorns, nuts!' Thus he spoke, the Marumda.

"After that Marumda floated away to the north, singing all the while a wishing song . . .

"Now Marumda walked around all over the earth, saying: 'Here will be a mountain, here will be rocks, there will be clover, here will be a valley, there will be a lake, there will be crops, here will be a playground, there will be crops, here will be a clover flat, there will be a grain valley, on this mountain there will be acorns, on that one manzanita, juniper berries; on this mountain there will be potatoes, deer, hare, rabbits; on that mountain there will be bear, puma, cougar, fisher, coon, wolf, coyote, fox, skunk; on this mountain there will be rattlesnake, king snake, gopher snake, red-striped snake, mountain garter snake, blue snake, big gopher snake.'

"Marumda walked over the hill; on the other side it was dark; he sat down; there was no light. He went on. Up in the sky there was light. Then he rolled the earth over, it turned over, he pushed it over: 'This is the way you will perform,' said the Marumda, 'now it is dark, and now it is light, and now it is sunlight.' Thus it performed . . .

"And then he went on and made a mountain: 'On this there will be sugar pine.' And then he went on and made a pond: 'Here there will be all kinds of fowl.' And he went on and made a mountain of flint: 'This will be arrowheads and spearheads.' And then he went on and made a mountain of drill flint. After that he went on and made a spring, and on either side he put sedge, rushes, redbud bushes: 'This will be for the women to weave their baskets; dogwood, white willow, black willow, wherewith to weave.' And then he went on and made wild nutmeg: 'This will be bow wood.' After that he made another kind of dogwood: 'This will be arrow wood, mountain bitterweed.'

"After this Marumda went on the other way, he went on and on, and then he thought of making Big Mountain. He did just that and on each side he made a large river: 'This will be for the fish to come out to the lake.' Thereupon he went on and made a wide valley: 'Here will be all kinds of crops.' Thus he said, the Marumda.

"And now he arrived at the lake, and going along the shore he made rocks, he makes them, and: 'This will be a playground for the water bears.' Thereupon he went on and made a sandflat, and then: 'This will be a playground for people.' Thereafter he went on and made a mountain: 'Here people will not come! Never approach this place!' Thus he said, the Marumda . . .

"He sat down by the side of the water, and he looked about, and then he thought to experiment at making people. 'Wah! What shall I make people with,' he said. 'Eh,' he said, and he picked up rocks: 'These will be people!'

"These rocks became people. They spoke a language. They were short-legged, these rock-people. These rock-people lived in the mountains only. They did not walk about in the valleys.

"Then he experimented making other kinds of people. The rock-people were mean, that's why he experimented making other people. He made people out of hair. These people were long-haired; and hair came down to their feet . . .

"After this he experimented making still another kind of people: 'Wah! What shall I make them of now?' he said. He went to a big valley toward where the sun rises. Here he made people out of flint. These were the Gilak people. He made this people on the mountain where there are nothing but rocks.

"These people were like birds flying in the sky. They used to swoop down on people. They had not been taught to do that way. They were mean people.

"All these were the first people that the Marumda made.

"Then he went north to his abode. Time passed, time passed, time passed, time passed, and then Marumda saw in a dream that the people were behaving badly. So he decided to go to his elder brother. Then the cloud-house started to float. Eight days it floated, the cloud-house, and then it reached the Kuksu's house.

"Four times he floated around it and then knocked at the door. Then the Kuksu opened the door and Marumda went in. Then the Kuksu said: 'What is it, younger brother?' Thus he said, the Kuksu.

"Then Marumda said: 'Oh! It's all wrong! I have come to consult you. The people that we made are behaving wrongly. They are intermarrying, they are turning into idiots, and their children grow puny. Therefore I will wash them away!' thus he said, the Marumda.

"Then Kuksu spoke: 'Wah! It's all wrong! We never taught them to do this!' Then Marumda spoke: 'Our people have become like birds, they have become like deer! They sleep with their own children. This is too bad! Therefore I am going to wash them away!'

"Then in no time the skies clouded up, the thunder spoke, and rain began to fall. For four days it rained; it became a flood. Marumda himself was running around among the rocks. Finally he ran for refuge to the top of the mountain peak.

"After every person had been destroyed, and there did not

remain a single person, Marumda called four times. He walked along the shore, he sat down and looked around. 'Here there will be a large village,' he said. Then he went on, he goes on, and again he returned and once more he looked around. Where a while ago there had been nobody, now a big village existed.

"Time passed, time passed, time passed, time passed and then the people began again their incestuous ways. And Marumda knew by a dream that his people were doing wrong. 'Wah! That's not the way I taught them to do! I will go and consult my elder brother about this!'

"Four times he made us people. First he drowned them in the water. Then he destroyed them by fire. Then he destroyed them by snow. Then he destroyed them by a whirlwind. Thus he destroyed them four times. After the fourth and last time he destroyed the people . . ."

The old man glanced at his grandson; the boy was wide awake. He estimated the length of the history he was recounting and decided to insert a few more episodes. It was possible to tell one episode or string together all of the episodes and thus recount the entire history of his people, according to the situation. He decided to keep the history short tonight.

"Marumda started to look for people. 'Have all the people been destroyed?' he said as he went along. 'Oh! There must be many peoples on this earth. They will speak different languages. They will be different in color, the people on this earth!'

"And then he went eastward, the Marumda. He arrived at a large valley and walked around it. 'Wah!' he said, 'why are there no people here? Here there will be a village.' There he dug a small hole, and all around he planted the sticks. . .

"At daybreak where he had planted the sticks it sounded like people talking among themselves. 'Eh! What I planned will stand true!' he said, and he went over. As he was nearing the round-house a man came out the door. 'Where are you going?' he asked.

" 'I have come to see how the villages are doing. In this valley you will hunt your food!' Then the man called to the people inside and they came out. 'How are we to hunt food?' asked the leader.

" 'That's what I have come to teach you. Break off some of

that wood over there and bring it here.' Then the man who was in front of the others broke off some of the wood and brought it back. 'Now break off some little ones and bring them here!' Then that man broke off some little sticks and brought them back.

"Then Marumda split the large piece of wood and scraped it and in no time he made a bow of it. Then he peeled the little ones and made arrows out of them. Then: 'Bring some flint from over there!' he said. He chipped with his teeth the flint, and in no time he made arrowheads out of it. Then he felt in his little dried-up sack and brought out some sinew.

"He twirled a string, tied it to the bow, and pulled. 'This is called a bow,' he said. Then he felt in his little dried-up sack and brought out some feathers, he split them, and tied them to the end of the arrows. Then he fixed the flint arrowheads. 'With this you will hunt deer,' he said.

"Then he said to the women: 'Over there there is kuhum.'

" 'What is kuhum?' they asked.

"Then Marumda went to dig some and brought it back. 'This is weaving material for you.' He also brought some willow roots. 'With these you will make baskets. Over on that mountain there are trees with acorns. These are food for you. In that river over there there is fish for you to catch with nets. Thus you will live.'

He felt in the little sack hung around his neck and brought out a string. Then he started a net and in no time he wove a long one. 'This is a seine,' he said. Then he wove a fish-trap. 'You will make a dam in yonder river, you will place this trap in it and then you will drive the fish into it.'

"Then he picked up a rock and pecked it, and in no time he made a pestle. Then he brought out a flat rock. 'This is called a metate, for pounding seeds and acorns.' Then after a while he said: 'Now I am going. Live righteously and your people will be healthy!' Thus he said and he went on."

Wakim listened attentively. He always enjoyed hearing the religious history of his people and the sonorous cadences of the ceremonial language which flowed from the speaker melodiously.

"In this fashion he went around the world," the old man said. "Wherever there was a good place he made a village. He went where he had first made people. 'Are you living well?' he asked.

"'Yes, we are living well. But where have you been?'

"'Just a little way.'

"'Are there other people like us?'

"'Yes, lots of them! There are people far from here whose language you don't understand. They speak different languages. They live on the other side of that mountain. They speak nearly like you. You must make friends with them.'

"Then he went off. He went over the hill to where there was a big valley and he walked around it. 'Here also there must be a village!' he said. He brought some willow wands to the middle of the valley and there he dug a little hole. Then he split the wands with his teeth. He took some charcoal and crushed it. Then he painted the sticks with it.

"'This one will be the song leader. These will be the chorus. These will be the dancers. These will be the women dancers.'

"Then Marumda spoke: 'This is what you people are going to do. You are going to gather your provisions, your venison meat, your acorns, your valley seeds. Then you will store them away, and on this you will live in abundance. You will hold festivals. When visitors come from a distance, take them into the house and partake of food with them. When your friends come from somewhere to visit you, that's the way you must provide them with food.

"'There are going to be many of you people. Therefore you must take care of each other. Therefore you must claim one another as friends, you must claim one another as relatives. Thus you will live in happiness!' Thus spoke the Marumda. And then he departed.

"Thus it was that people got acquainted with one another. They acknowledged one another as friends and relations. The young men hunted deer and caught fish. They gathered acorns. They carried and brought food in to dry, and deer, and fish. Thus they did. . .

"In this wise he visited every village, teaching them how to perform the dances. Eight days and eight nights he would perform, and then it was completed.

"After this he walked about on a mountain, and he called

together the coyotes: 'You will watch over the villages that are strung out on the land. If enemies should approach, you must cry: Guhma a'a . . . guhma a'a . . . enemies . . . enemies . . .' Thus the Marumda instructed the coyotes.

"After this he called together the wolves of the woods: 'You will travel in the woods, hunting your food!' Thus he instructed them.

"Then he called together the wiq'a: 'You will travel amid the rocks hunting your food!' Thus he instructed them. And then he called together the pumas: 'You will travel on the mountains, hunting your food!' Thus he instructed them.

"Then he called together the skunks. They came out with their tails over their heads. There was some noise, and they squirted in that direction, making the whole land stink as they came: 'You mustn't do that!' said Marumda. 'Only if they threaten to kill you, then you may do it! You will live in holes in the rocks and in the trees.' Thus he instructed them.

"Then he called together the raccoons: 'You will live in holes in the trees and there you will hunt your food.' Then he called together the squirrels: 'You will build your nests high up in the trees and from there you will go and hunt your food!' Thus he instructed them . . .

"Then he called together the rabbits: 'You will live in the valleys and in the mountains.' Thus he instructed them. After this he called together the ground squirrels, the moles, the gophers, the field mice, the wood rats, the badgers: 'You will dwell under the ground, you will live in holes!' Thus he instructed them.

"Then he called together the rattlesnakes, the large gopher snakes, the small gopher snakes, the milk snakes, the red-striped snakes, the mountain garter snakes, the snakes with green back and red belly, the big lizards, the common lizards, the salamanders, the giant salamanders, the snails: 'You will live in the hills, amid the rocks, in the trees, in holes underground!' Thus he instructed them.

"Then he called together the birds, the eagles, the condors, the hawks, the falcons, the goshawks, the kites, the big horned owls, the ground owls: 'You will live in the hills, in hollow trees, in holes in the rocks." Thus he instructed them.

"Then he called together the bluejays, the blackbirds, the quail, the crows, the flickers, the red-headed woodpeckers, the mountain jays, the grouse, the robins, the mountain robins, the towhees, the black-and-yellow finches, the mountain quail, the road runners, the ravens, the sapsuckers, the woodpeckers, the thrushes, the blue birds, the swallows—all of them he called together and instructed them: 'You will live in the hills and the valleys, and in hollow trees!' Thus he instructed them.

"Then he called together the water birds, blue heron, sand-hill crane, white crane, bittern, little green heron, swan, goose, mallard, cormorant, grebe, merganser, sea gull, piedbilled grebe, little merganser, mud hen, he called them together and addressed them: 'In the water you will live, in the water you will seek your food!'

"Then he called together the fishes: 'Fishes who live in the water, all of you come ashore!' Thus he spoke. Then Turtle came ashore first, and behind him came all the fishes. 'You are not a fish!' said Marumda to the Turtle. 'You will travel on the land. You fish, you are not to travel on land! You fish, you must live in the water. You will eat food from the water. And you too, Turtle!' Thus he spoke. Then the fish went back into the water, and Turtle floated back into the water.

"Thus sitting on the top of a mountain spoke the Marumda. Thus he instructed everything on the earth. How they were to behave, what they were to eat, where they were to live, he told them that way, everything. That's what he called them together for.

"He sat on a large flat rock on top of the mountain, giving instructions to everything that lives. Then he got off and stood the rock on edge. 'People must never come here!' Thus spoke the Marumda.

"Then he departed. 'If people come here this rock will fall and the people will live no longer! If anyone comes here he will die forever!' Thus spoke Marumda . . ."

The old man saw that he had judged well the endurance and interest of Little Boy. He closed the history with the proper and traditional ending, "From the east and from the west may the Daylight Ducks come quickly and bring the daylight soon."

Little Boy was almost asleep, but the ending had interested

him. In a sleepy voice he asked, "What are the Daylight Ducks, Grandfather? And why do you always end the same way?"

"This is our way of ending. It makes the daylight come quickly. Daylight Ducks are bright shiny white ducks whose every move produces a little light. Then, as the dawn creeps over the hills to the East, they vanish. Very few people have ever seen them. They come only at certain seasons." The old man stretched and yawned. "Now it is late." Then he turned to the youngster. "Come, it's time to sleep."

Man of Many Beads had participated in the various conversations all evening, trying to convey the impression that nothing of consequence had happened. Most of the other young men had gone home to their wives. As he sat thinking about what had occurred, his eyes took on a dreamy look and his face became impassive. He was thinking that Long Haired Woman had said nothing to him about his offense; yet there was no question but that she had seen him or at least had heard about his behavior from one of her relatives.

Then he thought of the other woman and what had passed between them. He was sorry in some ways because it had led to difficulties, but at the same time a warm glow started to spread through his body. As he kept thinking he became more anxious to smooth things over with Long Haired Woman.

He looked around and saw that everything was quiet. Making no sound, he arose casually as if he were merely going out to take care of nature's call. He wanted to avoid notice, for a remark would make it embarrassing for him to stay away for any length of time. Once outside, he walked a few paces, indecisively, towards his house. Perhaps Long Haired Woman would not speak to him if he returned. On the other hand she could create a scene in the crowded household. Maybe he should wait a while until her anger cooled. But her punishment had not been severe, and his desire for her was too great to be denied for very long.

He quickened his pace and continued towards the house, entered, and, once inside, stopped. Again indecision had struck him. All was quiet except for the snores, occasional coughs, and the other sounds of the night. He could barely discern the various sleeping quarters, each of which contained a small

63

family, all of whom made up the big family. He could see each family fire, however; some showed only embers, others still had some flames dancing about. He stood, uncertain, until his eyes started to smart from the smoke; then he went over to his own area: it was empty. He was about to leave, when he heard the voice of his wife's grandmother.

"She lies here with me," said the old woman. "She is asleep."

Man of Many Beads grunted and left the house. "So she is going to do it that way," he thought. When a wife wanted to keep her husband away, she would go to bed with another female, one taboo to the husband. Man of Many Beads looked longingly at the hut, then turned back toward the sweathouse.

He wanted very much to speak with someone congenial and sympathetic. Almost without realizing it, he turned towards his *awihinawa's* house, and slowly walked past the entrance to his cubicle. It was late, and all was quiet inside. Why hadn't he come here sooner? Now he would have to wait until the next day, for in awakening *awihinawa* he might awaken the entire household and cause further talk in the village. In his anxiety he had forgotten that *awihinawa* was taboo, and he had also not thought that in the dark he would not be at once recognized and might be suspected of intent to poison.

He felt frustrated and angry; there was nothing he could safely do. He needed to resolve his problem, and soon. His *awihinawa* might have had some ideas of how to settle the matter. Any delay would make the breach more difficult to mend. In one way he was sorry he had gone back to Long Haired Woman so soon. On the other hand it was best to smooth over difficulties as quickly as possible; otherwise both families would become tense and strained which might lead to greater difficulties for all concerned. He returned to the sweathouse, stretched out near the fire, wrapped himself in his blankets, and although he tossed and turned in troubled thought, was nevertheless soon asleep.

Chapter V

IN the morning the men and old women chatted as they left the sweathouse to go home for their morning meal. Man of Many Beads slowly strolled in the direction of his mother's house. He was hungry, yet he hesitated, wondering what his family's attitude would be. He knew the speed with which news traveled and that it must certainly have reached his relatives. He wished it were possible to go somewhere on a trip and avoid the difficult situation. But there was no escape; he would have to stay in the valley until his eyebrows grew back or some other event in the village directed attention away from himself. Meanwhile, to face either family with his plucked eyebrows would be uncomfortable.

It was not uncommon for a married man to drop in on his mother's family occasionally. The easy arrangement allowed relatives to keep apart gracefully, yet it was a help in bringing pressure to bear from both families for a rapid and amicable settlement of differences.

He entered his mother's house and sat down. His old grandmother passed some food to him and said, "It is fine to see so clean a face, but sometimes there is more trouble with a clean face than a dirty one."

Man of Many Beads kept quiet, while all eyes turned toward him. The husbands of the women were seldom pleased by their wives' male relatives coming back to live or even visit in the house, and many of the women felt the same way. Such a visit provoked undercurrents of tension, since it indicated at least the potentiality for grave trouble which might involve huge expenditures of wealth, food, and energy.

As he gulped his food his grandmother said, "When you finish, you must go back to your wife's house for additional breakfast. Two breakfasts are good for young men."

"Ai, that is true," said the Head Man of the family.

It was clear that Man of Many Beads was expected to go back to Long Haired Woman immediately. He rose and left.

He would have liked to see his *awihinawa* first, but he had to go to his wife, and it was best to arrive before the family had dispersed.

Long Haired Woman was still not in their cubicle. He said to her grandmother, "Old Woman, where is Long Haired Woman?"

"She has left the house," said the Old Woman.

Man of Many Beads went outdoors. Although he was disappointed, he felt better. Now that he had made a daylight appearance he had satisfied the injunctions laid down by his family. He went towards the sweathouse; a few old men and their young companions were sitting outside it in the warm sun.

The storytelling had been resumed. Youngster was saying to his old grandfather, "Last night I told you about the hills and how I would like to go there. Tell me, Grandfather, what lies beyond them?"

The old man nodded his head at the horizon. "Beyond those hills there are the mountains, as you can see. Beyond those mountains lie other mountains—and then there are more mountains, until you come to the ocean. In those mountains there are forests you have never yet seen the like of. The great trees you see in this valley are like bushes compared with the great redwood trees. When you go through the forest it is dark and mysterious. No people live there; one cannot even find any animals there. Very few of us ever go into those distant valley forests; we travel along the ridges of the mountains when we go to the ocean to get food and salt.

"In the ocean we find abalone and mussels, and the sea otter whose skin makes the finest clothing. Salt can be scraped off the rocks, and in the fall of the year many berries ripen for gathering. We know that when we go there we will always find food.

"During times of starvation our strongest men and women start out with great baskets, traveling constantly. At the coast they gather as much food as they can carry, eat plenty while they are there, and return home as quickly as possible. On their return, the food is distributed by the chief to all the people according to their needs. The people in turn give money to the chief, who then passes it on to the travelers, who then have a Big-Time."

"Ai, Grandfather. I've seen the Big-Time and enjoyed that food. I like best the seaweed that's cooked in the ashes, and the abalone—oh, I like all the feasting and dancing of the Big-Time."

The old man looked down at the lush, green valley with its many pools left behind by the receding flood. The foothills and ravines, with their intervening spurs and hogbacks, extended as far as the eye could see.

"The valleys in the region to the west are not like this valley. It's easy to walk here once the rains have stopped. But in those other valleys, there is no flat land at all. The underbrush and trees are so thick, the ground so uneven, that it's hard to get about. It is a long tiresome journey to the coast and back, and dangerous, too. There are many supernaturals, and we have to pass through the land of the Icheche, who allow us to get food on the coast. There you can meet Cloud-Man and Fog-Man, who are two of the six servants of Marumda, and, of course, you can always meet Bagil who, as you know, is very dangerous. But everyone's joy when the expedition returns makes all the danger worthwhile. When we get to the coast we make rafts and then go out to the seal rocks to get sea otters. Ai, it is hard work, but we like to do that."

"What is it like over there, Grandfather?" asked the youngster eagerly. "What is the sea like, and the land?"

The old man's eyes became withdrawn as the scenes floated back from memory. "The sea is a vast heaving mass, all one can see is moving water. And beyond the sea lives Water-Occupation.

"The water is salt to the taste. We go about brushing salt from the rocks until we have collected a lot of it. Then we purify it in the fire before we bring it home.

"Swimming in that water is very different from what we know here. It is easier to stay afloat in the sea but the salt stings the eyes.

"The sea has eaten away much of the land, which is rocky, and sometimes drops hundreds of feet straight into the sea. There are coves with beautiful sandy beaches, inlets, and rivers. At the top of the cliffs in some places there is a shelf of land which is flat, and sometimes as much as a mile wide. There is a mountain that runs parallel to the coast in a continuous range, except where a few rivers have broken through.

"There are also many streams that have cut into the mountainsides. It is almost always very foggy and wet and cold there. Even in the hottest summer in this valley, you may find a heavy, cold fog and rain on the coast. But sometimes it's hot, and the sun shines. One never knows what kind of weather one will find. There aren't many acorns or deer, but you can often find wild duck and other wild fowl, and always the food we get from the sea. Before we start, the old fisherman looks at the stars and tells us when the tide will be at its lowest, which is when we can get the most abalone."

"I would like to see that sometime," said the youngster. "It sounds so different from our valley."

"I would like to see it all again myself, but we won't be able to until we go there for a Big-Time." The old man's eyes narrowed, as if in memory he were standing on a headland looking out on that distant sea.

"Yes, the coast is beautiful. From a hill you can see the green-blue water, and the white foamy waves breaking continuously against the bright-colored rocky shores. There are long white beaches, inlets, pools, flowers of many colors, green hills and trees, and the sailing white clouds."

"If it is so wonderful there and there's so much food, why don't we go and live there?" asked the young boy.

"Very few people live on the coast because the weather is so bad there. It is much better to live over the first mountain, where one is protected from the fog, rain, and cold. It is easier to travel and to hunt along the mountain ridge, too, but it's impossible to travel along the shore because most of the coast is a sharp cliff which the waves beat against. In many places it's undercut with tunnels and there are many masses of fallen rocks where the undercut cliffs have slid into the sea. And sometimes you come upon rivers and streams and must go far inland before you can cross them, but as soon as you get over the first ridge it is much easier.

"Those mountains run north and south along the coast to the ends of the world, and very few people live in them. And between the coast and here there is a redwood forest over thirty miles wide. There are a few valleys where people could live, but it would be a struggle to find food. It's gloomy, although the forests are beautiful. Of course there is the Boonville Valley, which lies south and west of here. But that is a larger valley where people can live. They are our enemies, as you know," he added as if in an aside.

"This side of all those mountains are the valleys of the Russian River. Those south of us are very much like our own deep valley, but smaller. The Russian River runs through them from the north to the south, and finally turns west through the mountains to the Pacific Ocean.

"Many people live in these valleys, and they speak languages different from ours. But we never travel there except when we have our religious Big-Times, or to help mourn the death of a chief."

"Is the sea like the Clear Lake that you've told me about?" asked the Youngster.

"There is some similarity," said the Old Man. "But Clear Lake is fresh water and surrounded by land. As you go over our mountain and travel some distance toward the rising sun, you can see the entire lake lying in a tremendous valley. Our valley would be only a small part of that area. It is a long distance to that lake, and the people who live there live a little differently from us. At the southern end there are islands in the lake, and a whole tribe lives on each island, and other tribes live all around the lake. These people make canoes by tying tule together into bundles and then tying the bundles together into the shape of a canoe. They go all over the lake in these, fishing, for there are many fish, and many wild fowl live there too.

"When we are short of food we make advance arrangements

for a trading visit with these people. Sometimes we take our acorns and baskets, beads, money, skins, and other things to them to trade for their fish and wild fowl, and sometimes they come over here. Their houses are about the same as ours, just as the coast people's are somewhat like ours. The coast people make homes out of slabs of redwood bark, which we sometimes do also, but the Lake people do not use redwood bark but tule for their houses as well as their canoes."

"What is beyond the lake, Grandfather?" asked the youngster.

"Beyond that is another range of mountains, which is the end of the world to the east. The climate around that lake is pleasant, like ours, but there are many insects there, and it's very cold there in the winter and very hot in the summer."

"I would like to see that place, too, Grandfather. It must be nice to travel and see other places and people."

"Yes, it is nice, but you must remember always to be on your guard, just the same, against the unfamiliar supernaturals who are so dangerous, and all the strangers who may poison you."

"Where did all those mountains, the ocean, and the other things come from?"

"How many times have I told you that I can't tell you such things during the daytime? I'd become humpbacked if I did," said the old man.

Chapter VI

FARTHER along the circle another old man paused in his talking; the firelight flickered, and the shadows chased one another over his face, which had grown pensive. After a bit his young man companion said, "Grandfather, what are you thinking about?"

The old man said, "I was thinking how the years have passed since I was a young man like you. The years are so much alike that it's difficult to remember exactly when anything happened, the religious get-togethers in the different valleys that take place once in every seven years, the deaths of my relatives, the marriages and births, and things of that sort. Then I also remember the bad years when food was scarce, and we had to make many trips for supplies to the coast and to Clear Lake. But most of all I was thinking that we shall soon be moving to the river again because the sun is getting hot and the streams are subsiding.

"I was thinking of how we move three times every year. During the winter we live in our houses in this village. It is a time of ease because we have prepared and stored our food supply, the wood for our fires, skins for making into blankets and clothing, roots for the women to make baskets of, and clamshells from which to make money, as well as many other things. Yes, it is a time of ease, but also a time of inactivity because the ground gets so soft and muddy, the streams become rivers, and the rivers lakes, and it is difficult and disagreeable to hunt or fish or to move about. It's also the time when people cannot

71

get away from one another, and difficulties arise. They growl at one another and fight, and although we are happy when the winter season starts because we are so comfortable, by the end of that period we are glad when it's time to move to the river bank because it has grown hot, and it's cool along the river, and it's easier for us to be together. The river is high enough for swimming and there are many fish, and in our lean-tos our eyes, which have become bloodshot and teary from the winter's fires and smoke, have a chance to become clear again. It seldom rains, and though the wind does not blow hard, there is always an evening breeze. The weather is so pleasant; it does get hot, but we rest in the shade and take a nap during the hottest part of the day, and at night it's always cool enough for blankets. My old bones stop aching, and I feel young again. There is a lot of food then because the grasses start growing, and it's easier to get rabbits, quail, and other animals. People live farther apart along the river bank under the trees. They are content and busy and don't bother one another, and they stop growling at one another. Fresh deer meat always tastes good, and there is a lot of it. Also there is very little that we have to carry to the summer camp, so moving there is easy and pleasant.

"Then as the hot season comes toward its end we look forward to the fall. I like that season very much too. We move away from the river then into the hills, and then each family is much by itself, and everyone roams all over the hills to pick the acorn, the buckeye, berries, grain, and other foods. We knock the acorns out of the trees, gather and roast them, and crack the hulls; we always have plenty of fresh acorns to eat. I like the ripe acorns best, though, the ones that don't have to be cooked.

"Sometimes I think this is the best season of the year. The food is most plentiful at this time, except during bad years when we have to store everything for the winter. But even then there are many berry patches, pine nuts, grass seeds, and other foods, and many of them have to be eaten when they're picked because they cannot be saved for the winter, like wormy acorns. But as the season goes on, the hard work tires old men like me because we have to work day and night to gather as much food as we can. Once the rains begin it is impossible to do that. Then the fallen acorns spoil, and it's hard to move around. By the end of that season we are both sorry and glad because then we must carry all of our accumulated food to our winter homes, and that's hard work. On the other hand, after spending the autumn at work, the husbands and wives get suspicious because it is so easy to meet others in the brush. We look forward to the winter village, where we will live in houses, meet in the sweat-house, tell stories at leisure, and enjoy ourselves. But then as the rains get bad and it gets cold and the mud gets thick, we start to yearn for the spring again.

"I was thinking how every new season is bright and pleasant, and how everyone looks forward to it, but then as each season continues, they feel differently. It is true that we like to see new faces and have new experiences—we get tired of the same people. Even if it is dangerous, we like to meet strangers. That is one of our troubles because only our relatives are safe. Although all relatives know this they get tired of one another and start to grumble and growl. It's good that we have these seasonal changes—they help to keep us in better spirits and to be happier than we would be otherwise."

The boy agreed. "Yes, Grandfather, I see what you mean. I too was thinking that as soon as the river is low it will be possible to cross the valley. I've wanted to get to the west side of the valley all winter long. Before the rains I could have done it anytime, but then I didn't want to. It's only since it's been impossible that I have wanted so much to get closer to those hills."

The old man said, "There is much food in those hills—acorns, deer, quail, and rabbit—but you must keep away from those hills unless you are with older men." He sighed.

"Ah, it is late; it is time to go to sleep now."

Chapter VII

MAN of Many Beads was restless. All this talk about the limits of the earth and the terrain was boring to him; he'd heard it many times before and had visited almost every place the old man had mentioned at least once, on a trading expedition, a war party, a religious ceremony, a food expedition, or in order to acquire raw products for the various industries. All this time he had been hoping his *awihinawa* would appear. Now he decided to seek him out.

When he came close to the entrance to his *awihinawa's* cubicle, he stopped and said, "Ah ey, ah-aha, ah ey, ah-aha. It is I, it is I, don't be afraid."

"Come in, come in," called the *awihinawa.*

Man of Many Beads entered and stood to one side of the door as was the custom.

"Rest yourself right here," said his *awihinawa.*

An old woman gave him some food. Man of Many Beads disliked this ritual and he knew that *awihinawa* felt the same as he did about it. The old woman had given him some mush, which meant that meat was still taboo for *awihinawa.* He said, "Come, let us go outside. Must you stay here?"

"My wife is still month-sick," said *awihinawa.*

If he had been anyone else, Man of Many Beads would have left immediately since his power would have been violated by the situation. But he was not planning to hunt or gamble today and would take a cleansing plunge in the river before he went back to the sweathouse.

They stood up, walked together out of doors and strolled toward the hills. Under ordinary circumstances *awihinawa* would have remained at home with his wife. *Awihinawa* commented laughingly, "You have a nice clean face. Long Haired Woman did a perfect job."

"Isn't it enough that I must take this joking from all the other men?" Man of Many Beads asked angrily. "Am I not shamed enough without your making it worse?"

As it was considered acceptable for *awihinawas* to show their true feelings to each other, *awihinawa* did not respond with anger; he only laughed again.

"Don't be angry. Tell me about it."

As they climbed the hill in back of the village, Man of Many Beads told his *awihinawa* about the previous night and that Long Haired Woman had gone to bed with her grandmother, leaving him no opportunity to make up with her.

When they reached the top of the hill they sat where they could look down upon the village and the valley. As they sat, silent or talking according to their mood, they could see people moving about on various errands. Man of Many Beads noticed his Elder Relative walking into the hills and wondered where he could be going.

The village occupied a shelf of land which pointed toward the river; a creek ran along a gully on its northern side. The houses looked like odd-shaped turtles moving downward toward the river in regular files, with streets in between each file. Some of the houses were round and dome-shaped, others oblong. The largest of the buildings housed as many as fifty people, all of whom were either close relatives or men who had married women of the household. There were a few small houses which held only a man and wife with their children or only women and children with perhaps one old man. Here and there were empty spaces where a house had been burned because the family Head Man had died. In the village were four larger depressions where assembly houses had originally stood, but had later been allowed to disintegrate. The assembly house now in use was in the center of the village, and nearby were the five sweathouses.

As Man of Many Beads watched the village from his vantage

point he saw the people busy at their various tasks. The weather was sufficiently damp now for making baskets; in the summer it was too hot, and the materials became tough and dry. A few women were sitting before their house talking, their fingers busily at work. Each had her own tools, a small obsidian knife with a blade as sharp as a razor, fastened to a handle with sinew, and a small bone awl made from the bone of a deer's leg, with a handle of beautifully carved manzanita.

Each woman's basketry materials were soaking nearby in a basket of water. Some were working carefully on gift baskets, which were actually a higher denomination of money, and which in the usual course of events would be traded many many times and eventually be placed upon the body of a person who was being cremated. Some were working on rough conical carrying baskets, used, with tump line over the forehead, for carrying great loads.

A Pomo Indian's life was involved with basketry. As an infant, wrapped and bound, he was cradled day and night in a baby basket. Every few days he would be taken out, unwrapped, and cleaned. As he grew older he would be left free in the cradle basket; after he had rolled the basket over a few times by himself, had climbed out, and had shown sufficient ability to move about by himself, he would be free. When his mother went about he was hung in a basket on her back, held by a tump line. Even the house in which he lived was really a great thatched basket, and many of his toys were modeled after utility baskets.

His food was cooked in a basket; first the grain was put in it, then rocks heated in the fire were dropped in and stirred around until the mush was cooked. Grass seeds were put in a basket, hot manzanita embers dropped on top of them and all stirred together until the seeds were sufficiently roasted. His dish was a flat basket, his cup a round one. Acorns were pounded in a bottomless basket set onto a rock. Fish traps were baskets, as were seed beaters, winnowing devices, fences, summer shelters, bird traps and a great many household necessities.

One woman worked on a beautiful sun basket; her husband had killed hundreds of birds with his bow and arrow to get enough feathers for the one small basket.

The baskets were of all sizes and designs, the designs being decorative, without symbolic or religious meaning. Every woman selected her own patterns and intermingled the designs at will.

Some of the baskets were in an elongated boat-shape, some flat, some conical, some round; some were made with a coiled spiral of one stick; others with a coiled spiral of three sticks. The colors were a mingling of red, black, and creamy yellow-white.

As Man of Many Beads glanced about the village he noticed Old Man and Old Woman conversing at a little distance from their house, and fleetingly wondered what they could be talking about.

"Wait for me here," Old Woman was saying. She then went into the house, reappeared quickly, and said, "Let's go now." They walked away from the village into the brush. Old Man said, "Old Lady, what is important enough so that we must come here?"

"While we were talking back there I noticed a gray hair in your head," she answered. "It is something new, for I plucked your face only yesterday. Perhaps it was there, but I did not notice it. Undo your hair so I can see."

Old Man fearfully started to undo his hair; gray hair was one of the dreaded things among his people. He hoped that his wife had made a mistake, but he knew that she was generally careful in what she said. When his hair was undone Old Woman carefully parted it and searched. At last she said, "Yes, here is one." She kept searching and said, "Here is a second." After looking further she said, "Two are all you have. We can do nothing until you have four. We shall have to watch it carefully all the time. Fix your hair now, and I'll make sure that the gray doesn't show."

Old Man fixed his hair again with his wife's help. "Can't we use oak ball or pepperwood to dye the hair?" he asked her.

"We could, yes, but it's best not to do that now, even though I brought some with me. You have to be constantly reapplying it, and when there are a lot of gray hairs you can see the gray roots near the scalp anyway. We'd better wait and do it the right way; then you'll be rid of them completely, and we can transfer them to that old man who is our enemy. Let him be shamed."

Man of Many Beads could see fishermen, too, mending their nets, making and repairing their fish traps, and examining their fishing spears, some of which had a double toggle made of antler bone, attached with pitch and cord. They were much concerned, always, to keep their equipment in good shape, for fishing constituted one of the major professions in the community.

To be a professional was to be an honored man, and wealthy, and a provider of many important things for his family. An apprentice professional was much sought after in marriage, and for the most part these professionals were protected by large families.

He could also see some professional spear and arrowhead makers. Some were chipping the obsidian, some using their teeth to put a fine razor-sharp edge on the points. Off to one side there were some net makers at work, and in another spot some money manufacturers. They were all doing separate tasks: some breaking clam shells into rough squares, some chipping them into circular discs; others rubbing the discs on flat stones to flatten and whiten them; others were rotating long flint-tipped sticks between their hands, perforating the discs, which would then be strung on wire grass. Once strung, they would be rolled on a rock to smooth their edges and even their sizes.

The strings of small, fine beads or discs were usually given to the youngsters. The heel of the clam shell, sometimes as much as an inch thick, was considered heirloom money, to be expended only in emergencies.

This valley was the money-manufacturing center of the Pomo Universe. The men had to take an arduous journey over the mountains to the coast and then to the southwest to Bodega Bay to gather the shells themselves or trade for them with the local Indians.

In another part of the village, men were cutting rabbit skins into strips in preparation for twining them into blankets. Women were busy cleaning the skins, and sewing them into clothes.

Man of Many Beads said to *awihinawa*, "How suddenly the

village changes when the weather does. Everyone seems happy and content when there's so much work to do. A short time ago when it was raining everyone stayed indoors, and spent most of their time bickering and growling."

Beyond the hill on which they were sitting, they could see at some distance from the village the glistening, sweat-drenched bodies of men chopping and breaking wood, and the sounds of hidden men doing the same work reached them from an even greater distance. In the village itself old and infirm men worked under the direction of old women, whom they helped throughout the year. They picked acorns and berries, threshed seeds, helped make bread and dry salmon, and various other things which, for the most part, were considered beneath the dignity of men. These were the men who had never achieved professional status although since they had lived to be so old they were considered full of power and extremely dangerous to non-family members; they were therefore treated with great respect, out of fear of poisoning. Their own family members, on the other hand, who had no fear of being poisoned, treated them with little consideration because they had no wealth and could contribute very little food or money. Some of these old men were widowers, now living with their old sisters, who regarded them as encumbrances. Some were men who had remained with their families, but since their own sons had married out of the household and the majority of the men of their households were therefore strangers, they were in an unprivileged position in the household, exploited by the women and helpless to alter their condition. Although Man of Many Beads had never seen it happen, he had heard that in times of starvation, some families killed such old men, usually by strangling them with a stick set across their throats and kneeled on.

This would never happen to a professional; he retained some of his power and wealth until death; the old professionals were always treated with the greatest respect and controlled many of the tribe's most important activities. They helped in commonplace activities only voluntarily.

Man of Many Beads was of course proud and glad to be a professional. As he and *awihinawa* sat talking the life of the community went on entertainingly below them. The various groups of children playing their games made an especially attractive sight.

The games were of different sorts, mostly in imitation of adult activities. Some were hunters driving deer and quail. Others were playing the shinny game, knocking a hard wood ball around, yelling and screaming in their excitement. Some young girls were playing the women's game of marked sticks, in which six split sticks, flat on one side, round on the other, three marked and three unmarked, were used. A group was playing a game of jack-stones, throwing one object in the air and picking up as many other objects from the ground as they could before catching the thrown object on its way down; still others were playing cat's cradle. In one place a group of girls had a springy stick approximately six feet long; each girl inserted one end of it into a mound, bent it and let fly. The girl whose stick flew farthest was the winner. Another group was playing a game of tag; others had formed in a circle and were taking turns kicking a ball made of rushes and roots from one player to another within the circle. As a player missed or kicked the ball beyond the circle he was eliminated; the last person was therefore the winner. Other children were twirling tops made of acorns and sticks.

Another group of boys was playing arrow-throwing, a game in which each player had his own arrow, about three feet long and three-quarters of an inch thick. The arrow was thrown in such a way that it would glance off a mound and continue some distance beyond. The idea was to send the arrow as far as possible; the loser was cracked over the elbow by each of the other players; if he lost twice in a row he received two blows from each. Even when their arms became swollen and numb the boys did not give way, for that would be a sign of weakness.

"The other night there was talk about those creatures who raided the Lake People," said Man of Many Beads to his companion. "Some of the Old Men wanted to know if they were the Russians."

"That was a bad raid, I hear," said *awihinawa*. "But I can't believe the invaders were the Russians because they have always been friendly. We saw them on our trip to the coast two years ago. They hadn't treated those people roughly—in fact they've

81

been very good to them. They've built large houses of wood and large canoes that skim very fast over the water. While I was there I heard tales about other people, to the South, who acted like Gilyak. There were some who said they were Gilyak although others said they were only men. But that's all so far away it doesn't affect our people."

At that moment one of the boys raised his voice. He was gesticulating; there seemed to be some kind of argument going on. Suddenly there was a great deal of activity, and the boys began hitting one another with their sticks and yelling. Some even picked up stones and clubs and used them in their anger. One of the boys was hit with a rock. By this time the families were erupting from their houses and converging upon the quarreling children. After a while the boys stopped fighting and became quieter, but then the older people began to shout and curse, and finally to fight. The men drew knives and the women spat in each other's faces and pulled each other's hair. Rocks flew and clubs were swung. By this time the rest of the community had rushed in and tried to separate the combatants and to quiet them down. As the Chief approached, he began to exhort them. "My people, you must be good to one another. You must not growl, you must not fight. You must take care of one another. It is not good for these things to happen. It is wrong." His voice was vibrant and sharp. "Such things lead to great trouble and bring shame upon us."

He went on speaking in this fashion for more than half an hour. Gradually his voice became sonorous and soothing with a well-defined traditional cadence. Finally the squabblers became quiescent and no longer struggled against the people who held them back. Then the Chief said, "Now this has happened, now it is over. We must be friends; we must forget these quarrels and continue with our work."

The people dispersed and started back to their homes.

But *awihinawa* said, "Now there'll be more trouble. Nobody forgets; it's always bad when things like this happen."

"That is so," Man of Many Beads replied, "but they don't happen very often. There are a few people here who make trouble all the time, but they'll be taken care of. My grandfather told me about a woman who was old when he was a young man. She was always growling at people. She would even stand in the rain and growl at the other women and keep saying all kinds of bad things until they would answer back in anger. The old woman's relatives tried to get her to stop, but they couldn't. The people were afraid of her; she was an old woman, full of power and mean. They talked so much about her and hated her so that finally someone poisoned her to get rid of her."

"Yes, I've heard stories like that myself," said *awihinawa*. "My grandfather used to tell me about Bahap, a tough man who lived in Shanel, a mean fighter with a knife, rocks, or a club who used to kill people sometimes. When he killed a man his relatives would gather together a lot of money and give it to the dead man's family because they didn't want the family to think they were at fault. The first few he killed were people that his tribe did not like, they were bad, and that was all right; but then he killed a man who was not so bad, and his family gave the dead man's grandmother a huge basketful of money. Half of the money was given to the dead man's mother and the other half distributed among the relatives. Bahap's family were always afraid that they would be poisoned on his account.

"People actually paid him to kill, at times. Somebody finally poisoned him, too."

"Those people in Shanel are troublesome," said Man of Many Beads. "My grandfather told me that many years ago a group of their young boys got together and made trouble in the village. They mocked the old people, stole, broke up the earth oven, took some of the food, and ruined the rest, and did many other bad things. My grandfather had never heard of another such case. When enough people started to complain seriously, the heads of the families went to the Chief, who called a council together; they decided to get rid of these boys. The War Chief got together the tribe's best warriors, best fighters, and best runners, and the boys were rounded up from their homes. Then the War Chief said to them, 'Leave here, and don't ever come back; we don't want you.' They drove them out like sheep, and they never came back."

"We once had a case like that here," said *awihinawa*. "You know about that family that lives off in the hills, the one that was always making trouble and that never listened to what the Chief said? A Council was called then too, and it was decided to drive them out of the territory in that same way. No one has seen any of them since."

"It is too bad when these things happen among our own people—as if we didn't have enough to think about and to be careful of with all the different tribes in the other valleys."

"You remember the time some years ago when those two Head Men got into trouble? They had always told their grandchildren never to joke about important things, but one of them, relying upon the close friendship between the two, said to the other, using the name of a dead relative, 'Your relative was a bad man,' which, of course, is a terrible insult. Then they started yelling at each other.

"The chief came along and said, 'My children, don't do that, for I shall be ashamed.' He spoke to them for a long time. Remember how we felt at that time, how terrible it was for two Head Men to quarrel in public? That could really split the entire tribe and cause all kinds of difficulties."

After a pause Man of Many Beads said, "I wonder what would have happened if they hadn't stopped. My grandfather said in such cases the other Head Men would decide that the man who started the fight would have to give the other man a fine present and a big feed. That actually happened once, long ago. They decided that if the guilty man did not pay he would be kept out of the council and tribal affairs, and if he continued to make trouble, he and his family would be driven out of the territory. There have been cases in the past where two people have settled arguments with a bow and arrow. My grandfather himself didn't know of any, but he had heard of them from his old relatives."

"I know that people have hurt each other in that way," said *awihinawa*. "My grandfather told me that long ago they had a rough man here who had been bad even as a child. They used to punish him by making him carry loads of wood for the sweathouse. They used to make us do that when we were bad too. But none of the usual punishments had any effect. He kept doing mean things and making trouble. Finally they put hot coals in his hand and closed his fingers over them. You and I have both seen such punishments imposed, even though they're very seldom necessary. Even that did no good and he continued to embroil his family in difficulties until his family paid some northerners to kill him. They shot him with an arrow when he was out in the hills. Although it had all been prearranged, it was done in secret in order to keep tribal relations peaceable since, like every other person, the man was a member of two families, his mother's and his father's. After he was killed the northern tribe sent many presents. They claimed that their relative, a deer hunter, had shot at a buck, and that the arrow had struck the man accidentally. I asked my grandfather how they got the other tribe to do that. He said that you could only do it if you were related, that you could never trust anyone but a relative in such matters. It was claimed at the time that he must have broken some taboos, or the arrow wouldn't have hit him instead of the deer at which it was aimed."

Man of many beads said, "My grandfather has also talked about such things. He told me of cases in which men were driven from the valley, and in every case, since they were alone, were eventually killed by enemy raiders. But if the enemy had not killed them, they would have met a supernatural or a ghost anyway and, without anyone to work a cure, would have died. Some of these men were found all torn up, probably from meeting a bear, sometimes a real bear, sometimes a bear doctor. When bodies are found in that condition, no one pays any money to anybody. One man's body, I've heard, was found by people gathering roots for baskets. Everybody is glad when such matters are done with. But these are the only cases involving our tribal members that I can remember hearing about. Things don't usually go beyond the growling.

"The growling always seems to be worse at this time of the year though," he added. "Do you remember last year how those two families started growling one day and only stopped because the chief gave them a long speech? It started all over again the next day, and the chief stopped them again. Then it happened again on the third day. That night the chief spoke in private to the Head Men of the two families, and that was the end of the growling. No one knows exactly what he said. But my grandfather said that if they hadn't stopped, the council would have

85

decided which group was in the wrong and would have had it driven out of the valley."

"It's true," remarked *awihinawa*, "that when these things happen it's generally during this restless time of year. Everyone's too much afraid of the consequences since our people never forget an insult or an injury. My elder relations say that when you suspect hard feeling you must always start poisoning the other family first before they start on you. They say you must never let anyone know how you feel unless you are friendly, and you must never get too friendly either, for that will be a sign of weakness."

"It's bad always to have to be so careful," replied Man of Many Beads. "Every family has so many enemies, and it's so easy to acquire new enemies, which makes matters so much worse. Why does it always have to be that way between families? At least within the family it is a little better. Then you don't have to worry except when a new man marries into your group, and you have to be very careful until his first child is born. The family situation is different because there the old man and the old woman control things. If you don't do what's right you don't get presents, or food, and in general you're made to feel unwelcome. I remember when I was a young boy, two of the men in my family started to fight. The old Head Man ordered the other men to tie the two up and gag them, to let them cool off, and gave orders that no one should talk to them or go near them. He waited a long time, until they were really quiet and had had time to think. Then he started talking to them and went on for a couple of hours. Having to listen helplessly was worse than being tied up. After a time, he gave orders for them to be untied, repeated his injunctions to them to behave themselves and not create hard feelings. My family never had any trouble with them again.

"Of course what happens within a family is different from what happens between families. After all, one never uses poison on a family member.

"I remember a strange true story my grandmother told me about. She knew a man who used to growl all the time, and one day he made the mistake of growling at a great big strong fellow, who said to him, 'You are always making bad talk with that mouth of yours,' then grabbed the growler's mouth and tore it—just ripped it open. It must have been a horrible sight."

They fell quiet.

Awihinawa was thinking of the past four days of boredom, when he had had to sit in his cubicle at home with his wife, taking care of her and bringing her food, and being unable even to talk to a man for fear of taking away the other's power. He and his wife had eaten no fish, meat, or grease, only mush and grass seed, and they were allowed to drink water only before sunrise and after sunset. To be with his wife that constantly and to refrain from the usual actions of a married man, or even thoughts of sex, was almost impossible. He thought back to his premarital days when some of his age-grade friends had surreptitiously been intimate with unmarried girls and regretted that the taboos were so solid and unbreakable now that he was a married man.

After a silence he said, "Maybe it is better that Long Haired Woman slept with her grandmother. It's given both families time to think matters over, and it's better than if she had made a lot of trouble for you by doing something more severe. How about your relative? Did he find out that you were with his wife?"

"No," replied Man of Many Beads, "I don't think he knows, and he wouldn't care anyway. He is well known for trying such things himself. He'd even try to be with Long Haired Woman, but she would never allow him to come near her. He's tried to be with many women, but they usually laugh at him."

"Maybe so," said *awihinawa*, "but I have seen men get angry with him, and sometime he'll get into real trouble."

Evening was drawing near. They could see hunters returning from the hills, walking in single file with effortless grace, without swaying or bobbing. As they came close to the village, they followed one of the old paths. Although these paths had been used thousands of times, they were only the width of an Indian's foot and were worn down in some places as much as a foot and a half below the surrounding ground.

Some of the old men, accustomed to decades of long treks, moved with a relaxed, catlike, easy tread although they bore enormous loads of knobby tree limbs on their backs, burdens it didn't seem possible such old men could carry, let alone have chopped down in one day.

In the village itself there was the usual coming and going for that time of the day as the women went about their preparations for the evening meal.

Refreshed by each other's companionship, *awihinawa* and Man of Many Beads at last started toward the village, *awihinawa* to his wife and Man of Many Beads for the ceremonial plunge to wash away the taboo of having been with *awihinawa* at such a time.

Chapter VIII

THE brawl, initiated by the boys' fight, was the culmination of a long series of troubles in the village. The Chief was upset and worried, knowing that the incident would intensify and aggravate hostile feelings unless something happened to redirect the anger of the people, or unless the leaders took some action. He was well aware of the previous incidents, for the people had a subtle way of passing information along to him by way of slight hints from one relative to another until one of his close relatives or an assistant chief finally communicated the facts.

Rarely did anyone else come to him directly with information or blurt anything out in a blunt fashion. Lately he had been hearing about myths pertaining to poisoning and adultery, in increasing number. The afternoon fight was proof of the tension existing among the people. His only means of alleviating the troubles was by preaching morning and night. He himself could not institute action of any kind; he could only hope that the Head Men would take it upon themselves to initiate some action for everyone's benefit. At most he could drop vague hints to those Head Men whom he felt to be his strongest supporters. Anything more than a hint would be deeply resented and he would only get a negative response, and there'd be no council meeting.

The Head Man would feel that the Chief had overstepped the boundaries of his office and powers. It was always a very delicate matter for the Chief to exert his influence. Even when he was in favor of an action desired by some of the Head Men, he had to refrain from letting them know of his support; for, by the time it became proper to call a council meeting, a new factor might enter in to change their minds, or they might, after sounding out the attitudes of the other Head Men, discover that they were in the minority and drop the whole matter. The Chief would have to be right every time.

All he could do was drop some hints about general problems, but offer no solutions, to those assistant chiefs or Head Men who might start discussing the idea with the others in a general way. Only after their own discussions would they come to him and ask him to call a council meeting.

It was most difficult to know what would come of a hint, for one could never know which men were unable to participate. It was possible to know about the mourning periods of the various families, or some of the pregnancies, but not about the poisoning that was going on, and no Head Man would ask for a council meeting when he was in the midst of a poisoning situation, whether defensive or offensive. That was his time to stay at home and supervise all family activities. A hunt might be being planned, in which case the older Head Man would be involved in working with his group, or there might be a fishing or trading expedition in preparation. The situation required sensitivity to the feeling tones as well as the possible activities of the individuals involved.

The Chief strolled through the village, greeting people, and stopping occasionally to talk. Along the way he met one of his assistants, and as they walked together and talked, the Chief gradually, by insinuations and indirection, led the talk around to the recent troubles. At last the assistant asked, "Isn't there something that can be done?"

"Perhaps some of the Head Men are already discussing these matters," the Chief answered. "They may well be deciding to ask for a council meeting—I hope so."

This was a sufficient hint for the assistant chief; he understood that the chief wished him to deal with the matter delicately. The Chief called his assistants in to discuss matters only when preparations were underway that entailed intertribal activity. Then the Chief coached all his assistants, and their wives and sisters as well, in their proper duties and activities.

They parted, and the assistant chief went in the direction of the sweathouse, where he expected to find his *awihinawa* or his grandfather. He did find his grandfather and sat down to converse with him. After a while his grandfather said, "Today's excitement was not a good thing; a public brawl bodes trouble for us all."

"That's true," said his grandson. "Perhaps it would be a good idea for people to do something about all this."

"There are some who've already suggested that."

"Don't you think it's time for more serious talk so that something can actually be done about it?"

"Yes, you're right, there should be."

The assistant then changed the subject, and they continued to talk about other matters for a while.

When a Head Man approached and sat down, the assistant wandered off. Discussions of this sort were seldom carried on openly, and he wished to be disassociated from it. Every effort was made to break the thread that might lead back to the Head Chief.

Conversation between the grandfather and the Head Man was general until the Head Man himself raised the question of the village difficulty.

The machinery was in motion.

The assistant searched further for his *awihinawa*. When they met they joked for a while, and then at last the assistant was able to bring up the subject of his concern, for his *awihinawa* was, after all, the one person upon whom he could rely for absolute secrecy and cooperation. He said, "If we keep having much more trouble, everybody will be fighting everybody else. It's time the Head Men got together and did something about it. Have the men of your family mentioned it?"

"Yes, there's been a little talk, but not very much; I think something will be done soon, though."

"It had better be soon," said the assistant. "Things are getting bad."

But already he felt better about the business, because he knew that by this time the Chief had approached the other assistant chiefs and that the grapevine was being utilized.

Chapter IX

MAN of Many Beads was just finishing the evening meal at his mother's house when Elder Relative staggered through the main door and fell to the ground. For a moment the household was still; then a crescendo of sound burst forth. The old men began giving orders, the old women wailed, and the babies and children, catching the excitement, began to cry.

The women, terror in their eyes, scratched their faces and breasts until the blood streamed and flung handful after handful of shell money into the air. Some women fell to the floor as if in a trance, and lay motionless. They were all attempting to induce the spirits who were taking away Elder Relative's essence to assault them instead, trying to distract the supernaturals and divide their attentions in order to overpower them and so win back Elder Relative.

Head Man sent three of the older men out of doors to act as guards, since it was common practice for a family's enemies to intensify their efforts to weaken it when a member fell ill, and it was then that the entire family was in greatest danger.

Everyone feared the power women, among others, whose evil could be negated only by the doctor.

The aged Head Man, chanting and praying, was examining Elder Relative. Immediately thereafter, he sent for the Kuksu doctor and for Elder Relative's wife who was at her own home and arranged for Elder Relative's care. Then, from his sacred bundle he took out the necessary articles, painted his body, and began to sing a ghost song. As he was a minor official of the

Ghost Society he knew enough of the symptoms to realize that Elder Relative had seen a ghost; immediate action was essential, or the man would die. He kept chanting while the men lifted Elder Relative off the floor.

Elder Relative's body was rigid and would not relax. The men moved him to a clear place and laid him down.

As Head Man chanted and beat time with his rattle, three other men took up the chorus and also beat time with their rattles. The women and children quieted down, and some of them began to massage the women who had fallen into a trance, who soon recovered and joined the others. Now all was quiet except for the chanting, praying, and singing.

The old Head Woman called the other old women together and told them to get rid of all fresh meat and fish. "We must have nothing around which was near us when we were month-sick," she said. "We must not think or dream either of these things or of sex. Tell this to all your daughters and granddaughters as well. Anyone who so much as thinks of sex or of getting month-sick must go to the menstrual hut. Remember that any kind of blood or the thought of it is very dangerous right now."

The doctor, accompanied by his three assistants, entered the house, examined Elder Relative carefully, and asked, "Where was Elder Relative going?"

The only one who knew was Elder Relative's wife. "He told me he was going hunting," she said.

"When did he leave?"

"When the sun was just above the eastern hills."

Knowing the length of time that had elapsed, the doctor could estimate how far Elder Relative might have gone. As a professional he was of course familiar with the specific abode of all the supernaturals. He asked, "Which direction did he take?" But the woman could not answer. "From which direction did he come?" was his next question.

Man of Many Beads remembered that he had seen Elder Relative going into the hills while he sat on the hilltop with his *awihinawa,* and spoke up, "I saw him going into the hills, up the ravine toward Big Mountain."

This was all the information the doctor managed to get. He deduced that if Elder Relative had indeed seen a ghost, Head

Man had already taken countermeasures. It seemed more probable to him, from the symptoms, that the sick man had encountered one of the many supernaturals who lived in the general area of Big Mountain. He therefore began to make a composite costume, representing the outstanding features of the various monsters he thought it most likely that Elder Relative had met.

While he made the costume, he chanted the specific prayers to each of the monsters involved. Meanwhile everyone was quiet.

The younger children were well back in the darkness against the sides of the house, as far away as possible from the contamination. The youths and maidens stood in front of them; and closest to the center of activity stood the old women and old men, who formed a ring around the doctors and Elder Relative. Anxiety and fright showed plainly in the rigid faces. The peculiar odor of human fear was seeping into the air, along with the odor of the angelica root that the men were chewing and with which they had also massaged Elder Relative.

Elder Relative's wife was thinking of the possible death of her husband, whom she loved. She was pregnant; perhaps that was why Elder Relative had met with the supernatural. If he died she would have to go into mourning; she would have her child without a father. As her fear increased, her eyes took on a glazed look, and her body became rigid. She was in a half-trance. Like the other women, she looked horrible with the blood spilling down her face and breasts from the lacerations made by her nails.

The Head Woman thought with dismay of this new trouble and its cost to the family. There was so much to do, so many taboos to observe. As soon as one period of taboos passed by, another came along; they were never free of them. "Ai! He must get well," she thought. "We shall place much wealth at the pole for the doctors."

Head Man, too, thought anxiously that Elder Relative must get well and hoped that his powerful ghost songs would help, along with the power of the doctors. He tried not to let his worry show, for he had to function as the leader by posture and demeanor. He stood like an image conveying confidence, wisdom, and power. All Head Men trained themselves for years to achieve a manner signifying dignity and power to their families and to the population in general, for it was in this way that they were able to exert control over the members of their households and gain respect in the councils. "It is good that he didn't collapse in the hills, for then he would have died before we could have found him," he thought.

And the doctor was thinking, "Another case, and again I must refrain from eating all meat and grease for at least eight days. It has been more than six moons since I have tasted the foods I enjoy the most. There are times I wish it were possible to refuse a case, but when I am called, I must go."

When all was ready the doctor instructed two of his assistants to prop the stricken man up. As they moved the patient they chanted, "I am going to carry this man. I am going to pack this man."

The doctor donned the costume representing the various monsters and went outside the house. At his signal, a shrill scream, the fire tender caused the fire to flare up, bringing all the details of the surroundings into sharp relief. Through the entranceway rushed the doctor dressed as a horrible monster, straight at Elder Relative, whose eyelids were forcibly held open by the doctor's assistants. Elder Relative's body convulsed, his back gave a cracking sound, and he began to shake all over.

Man of Many Beads, who had been unconsciously holding his breath, released it and relaxed. He saw and felt an answering relaxation of tension in the others. Elder Relative was now, at least to some extent, aware of this world and thus had some chance of recovery.

The proper songs were sung while Elder Relative was massaged until he appeared to be cognizant of the fact that he had been brought back from the afterworld. The doctor then took off his composite costume, making certain that Elder Relative saw him do so, thus relieving him of his fear. Elder Relative was still half-fainting and incapable of speech. The doctor watched the patient's face closely as he removed each portion of the costume, hoping to determine from his expression which particular supernatural he had encountered.

As soon as he had established that, the doctor instituted appropriate treatment, selecting the correct prayer songs from the more than one thousand available. He informed his assistants of the selection, and assigned duties to each.

The doctor hoped that Bagil, the water monster, was not involved, and that he had assigned responsibility for the disaster to the proper supernatural. Once he'd had a case in which a man who had also been hunting in the mountains had been frightened in the same way and collapsed. In that case the doctor had been sure that Bagil was involved, and it had taken an entire day to construct a model of that supernatural. He had first made a frame of sticks covered with tule and painted it black, white, and red. The eyes had been made of pieces of abalone shell; another piece of the shell hung from the mouth of the figure to catch the firelight and glitter when the monster moved. Yellow flicker feathers had been attached to the head. Finished, it was a horrible great snakelike creature six feet long and a foot wide. He had put medicine on it, *ya'na* and *ciyo'bat'-sum* and some of his own blood.

The patient had been covered with a blanket so that he could not watch the proceedings. Then a hole had been dug in the floor of the house and tule planted upright in it so that it appeared to be growing there, after which the hole was filled with water to make it look like a spring. The monster had been brought in and set in the center with its head raised by an attached string. The doctor, who was controlling the string, had hidden to one side. Another string, also attached to the monster's head, had been tied to a green stick stuck upright in the ground opposite the monster. When the doctor pulled the string the monster's head moved toward him, bending the green stick. When the doctor released his string, the green stick straightened up, pulling the monster's head away from the doctor.

At a signal, while the monster's head was manipulated by the doctor, the blanket had been removed from the sick man who, upon seeing the monster, went into a frenzy and fought so that six men had to hold him down although before that he had been too weak to move. After a struggle, he tired and then fainted. The doctor had sweated him, given him hot drinks, and bathed him with herbs to revive him, then sat down beside him and given him an account of his adventure. At dusk in the mountains, he had gone to slake his thirst at a spring, but before he could drink he had seen the monster, had turned, and run. He had started to feel strange before he reached the bottom of the hill and knew then what must have happened. Ever since, the monster had been haunting him. He had kept hearing it outside the house taking him away. Every time the patient had opened his mouth or batted his eyes, it had flashed just like fire.

That man had nevertheless recovered.

The doctor returned his thoughts to his present case.

The doctor and his assistants opened their bundles, the contents of which varied on the basis of the age and experience of the individual.

As he started to open his own sacred bundle, the doctor sang, "I am opening up. I am opening up, I am opening up. I am opening up." As he took each article out of the bundle he mentioned it in his chant four times.

The bundle contained a coyote's paw; obsidian knives used for cutting snakes and for splitting water dogs and other creatures; rabbit bladders filled with pebbles; four feather headdresses made from the feathers of very rare birds; a human bone called *tca'ya;* and various herbs, pastes, and other medicines.

All except the doctor and his assistants kept well back because each article was extremely powerful and would cause severe illness to the uninitiated person who came too close.

On the ground before him, the counting man had arranged bundles of sticks used to keep exact count of song sequences. The slightest mistake could spell death for his patient and cause the doctor and his assistants untold hardship. The gist of the songs was an imploring of supernaturals who were "friends" of the doctor to aid in the struggle with the malevolent supernaturals to win back the essence of this man and allow it to return to the body so that he would become well again. To some extent this was a contest between the doctor, an important Kuksu man of great religious training, and the malevolent supernatural. His power and ability were such that the great gods who had given him these attributes would aid him in the contest.

The doctor's life was one of service, and although he had become wealthy by means of his practice, his expenses were tremendous. He had constantly to reward and propitiate the gods. Every time he had occasion to open his bundle, whether for a religious ceremony or a cure, he had to give a Big-Time before it was put away again—a Big-Time involving a huge feast to which the entire village population was invited.

He started his first song. As he chanted he beat the rattle against his knees. One of his assistants continued to massage the patient's limbs, another sang and kept time with the head doctor, and the third, who was the counting man, dealt with his numerous bundles of sticks.

The sticks were arranged in four groups of fours, repeated four times. The small sticks were about two and a half inches long and about a quarter of an inch thick; the larger sticks were about the size of a man's pinky, but slightly narrower and longer. These made up a small bundle of four. There were still other and larger sticks to represent four fours and higher denominations.

The counting man had moved one stick as the doctor finished the song. As he began to repeat it the counting man moved another stick. At the end of the repeat the counting man called, "*Ho nani,*" or "Middle," and when the doctor began the song for the fourth time he called, "*Nani,*" the "end."

The doctor stopped. Beads of sweat, betraying the cost of his intense concentration, popped out on his forehead. He glanced anxiously at his patient; there had been no improvement. He looked around at the circle of watching, worried faces, then off into space. Doubts and fears filled his mind. With an accusing stare at the group, he said, "There is some woman in here who is month-sick or pregnant. Unless she leaves, this man will be lost. I shall be helpless and we shall all suffer. That woman must leave."

Everyone was still. No one moved as he stared at the stern, immobile faces. They simply stared back. He tried again.

"There is some woman here who is having thoughts of sex. That is dangerous. Or else some woman is month-sick or pregnant. I can do nothing until she leaves."

Head Woman was standing where she could see the patient's wife. She noticed her staring, glazed eyes, her trancelike expression and rigid body. She moved to the woman and said in a sharp biting voice, "You there." Slowly the woman's expression changed to one of comprehension.

The doctor was saying again, with more urgency than before, "One woman here is month-sick or with child. I implore her to leave!"

A look of understanding passed over the woman's face. She turned and walked quietly out of the house.

The doctor glanced at the counting sticks and took up where he had left off.

The songs and treatment went on and on, and the groups of sticks moved in accord with them.

As the singing and the beating of the rattle continued with regulated pauses, and the gods were importuned for aid, the tension in the family subsided and the odor of fear dissipated.

The patient gradually stirred into consciousness. It seemed that the words of the songs as well as the rhythm were having their effect upon him. As his glance wandered about he took in the quantity of money, blankets and baskets draped on the pole—a very reassuring sign to the old man, for when a family considered a person troublesome they hired a weak doctor and placed little money and few valuables on the post. He relaxed, breathing easily, secure in the knowledge that his family valued him.

Man of Many Beads had watched the proceedings with great interest and with growing admiration for the curative powers of the doctor. Once, when one of his relatives had been sick, a hole had been dug in the ground large enough to admit the patient. It had then been partly filled with rocks painted with red and black stripes, after which a fire was kindled in it and kept burning until the ground was thoroughly heated. Meanwhile the doctor had offered his prayers and sung his songs. The fire and stones were removed and a large quantity of rushes with their joints painted with the sacred red earth was thrown in and some damp grass laid on top to create steam. When all was ready the doctor stretched out on the grass, rolled over once, and then got up. The sick man was then placed on the grass and covered with hay and blankets. He perspired freely for some time.

He had soon recovered, although he had kept to the house for a few days longer.

The doctors set broken legs and arms and took care of all kinds of illnesses. They were not always successful; sometimes their patients died.

He wondered how the doctors chose the particular cure. He thought of a patient whom the doctor had brought partly out of the initial shock and then had laid on the ground. As the people sang, the patient's arms and legs were spread-eagled, and each limb tied to a springy twig that had been set firmly into the ground. Then the doctor, who in that case was painted spirally, approached the patient with a live coal on a fragment of bark. He burnt each of the four strings, allowing the twigs to spring up, one after another, and the patient had suddenly screamed out; the ties by means of which his essence had been held by Gilyak had been severed and he was well again.

And once an old woman had been found in a coma beside the brook. She had been drinking when she suddenly saw Bagil appear before her.

The doctor was able to bring her out of the initial shock, but her limbs then became inflamed. The doctor had then assembled all the people in the village who were not taboo at the time, and instructed them to lock hands in a circle around the woman on the ground. Then, at signal from the doctor, they began to dance around her while the doctor sang and kept time with his rattle. His assistants, who made up the chorus, also sang and accompanied him with other rattles. At first the singing was slow and mournful, as were the movements of the dance. There was no response from the sick woman, except for a continual groaning and a cry of *"Ahwe! Ahwe!"*

The tone of the chanting was full of sadness and commiseration as if the dancers were deeply moved by pity for the sufferer, but at the doctor's sign it quickened, and the dance gradually became more lively. Still she seemed unaware of their presence, and only continued to cry out piteously, *"Ahwe! Ahwe!"*

The tempo increased. The circle moved, first round one way, then the other, animation lighting the dancers' faces. At last the woman seemed to feel the contagious enthusiasm of the old familiar dance. The dancers circled still more swiftly. Her eyes began to brighten and soon she began to pulse with the rhythm of the music. Her wailing *"Ahwe! Ahwe!"* began to follow the ever quickening time of the chant. But still she was unable to rise. Upon signal the circle of dancers swerved suddenly, swooped upon her with shouts. She was caught up and half-carried, half-dragged around the ring, while her *"Ahwe! Ahwe!"* gradually changed into the general voice of the chanting and melted out of hearing, and step by step, feebly at first, but carried irresistibly away at last, she joined in the dance. She was well; she had returned.

The doctor had reached his last song.

Pipe and tobacco were brought forward. The pipe was lit and each adult male drew six mouthfuls of smoke, one for each group of supernaturals living at the four points of the compass and one for the earth and one for the heavens. Then the doctor and his assistants left. They would return the next night, the third night, and the fourth, when Elder Relative's cure, hopefully, would be complete, unless complications ensued from the activities of the family's enemies.

Chapter X

AS soon as the doctor and his assistants had gone, Head Man, indicating one man by a nod, said, "You, make the fires bright." To the others he said, "You, search everywhere for something bad."

Although the house had no partitions, each family group had its own cubicle and fireplace around the perimeter; a common aisle was left down the middle of the house.

The adult males immediately began searching every part of the house. Head Man turned to an older man who was Elder Relative's brother-in-law and said, "You, Elder Brother's wife's brother, go to your mother's house and seach Elder Relative's bed."

This was a case where an exchange marriage had occurred. After Elder Relative had married, the two families had decided that it would be advantageous to cement the two families more closely. Elder Relative's sister had therefore been given in marriage to his wife's brother. In this way neither household had lost a man or a woman.

The Old Man went to his parental home where he was received gravely. His sister had told the household about Elder Relative, and the men had instituted a search of the premises but had located nothing of importance. He went to Elder Relative's bed himself and felt under the straw. His search too was unrewarded. Then he searched the ground under the side of the house near Elder Relative's bed. As he searched he kept chanting powerful prayers. He used his left hand, for should he find anything dangerous and touch it with his right hand, he would become impregnated with the evil, whereas his left hand had the power to negate anything dangerous. Suddenly he tensed. He felt the ground again, carefully; it seemed to have been disturbed. He probed with his fingers and unearthed an object. He held it in his left hand as he chanted and then passed it to his right hand as he carried it close to the fire. The other men had become silent and had drawn near. He said, "Fix the fire."

One of the men put some kindling on the fire, which was still bright. The old man held the object out where the men could plainly see what he had found. It was a mountain lizard, the mouth and the anus of which had been sewn so that the lizard could neither eat nor defecate. It was obvious that some of Elder Relative's dung had been acquired by a poisoner and forced into the lizard, after which the orifices had been closed; a string made from the sinew of a coyote had been used to tie the lizard to a root in the ground. The idea was that as the lizard began to be miserable and sicken and to squirm in anguish, Elder Relative would do likewise. The sicker the lizard became, the sicker Elder Relative would become, until they both died.

Old Man said, "Do the women have any fresh meat? Elder Relative's family have disposed of all their fresh food."

The Head Man called to the Head Woman who was standing to the side, "Old Woman, you. Did you move all the meat out yet?"

"No," she said. "I have a rabbit here."

"Bring me a small piece, and then get rid of all the other fresh meat and fish in the house."

The old woman went to the end of the house and returned with the rabbit, which she gave to the Head Man, who took it with the usual precautions, and gave it to the old man; he hurried with it to Elder Relative's house. He stopped a short distance away and said softly to the guard, "Bring the Head Man to me." Both the lizard and the fresh meat would be extremely dangerous to Elder Relative; to bring them too close might prove fatal.

When the Head Man came out and saw what the old man had, he turned to the next oldest man and said, "You know what to do—cut it into strips."

The man followed his instructions.

Then Head Man said, "You three come with me."

He led the way out of the house and deep into the hills; it was only the direst emergency that would bring them to leave the village at night. When the old man arrived at a ravine deep in the hills he stopped. The group made a fire and tied the strips of meat to the lizard, after which the lizard was cremated with the same ritual as was accorded a human being. During the ceremony the men chanted the words, "This shall happen to the man who made this." During the entire cremation they kept repeating the phrase and crying and wailing as if they were mourning.

Then a hole was dug as if for the burial of the ashes of a dead person, and the lizard's ashes were interred while they all continued to pray, "This shall happen to the man who made this."

They carried out all the practices of mourning, after which they went down to the river and washed. They then returned to the house.

During the time that the Head Man was taking care of the lizard, the rest of the men continued the search, much of it out of doors. When they were sure that nothing unusual was about, they came indoors again, except for the guards on sentry duty.

During the absence of the Head Man and his helpers, Elder Relative had seemed more dead than alive. His glazed eyes remained open, but he was in a semi-comatose state. The doctor and his assistants had arrived, had dressed themselves ceremonially, and had begun again their performance of the previous day. In a little while Elder Relative, under the influence of the massaging, the chanting and the singing, began to show signs of consciousness.

The various members of the household were in their cubicles; the young men with their elder male relatives, the young girls with their female relatives.

Old Man had been waiting for the chance to leave the house, because it had been decided that he was to find a vantage point on one of the hills above the village and watch everyone's comings and goings. If it was observed that any particular individuals were deviating from their usual pursuits, they would of course be suspect. As soon as Head Man and his assistants entered the house Old Man turned to his grandson and said, "Come with me." This would be a good chance for the boy to acquire some useful knowledge.

They left the house, went towards the hills, and climbed a high knoll; at the top they secreted themselves in a small clump of manzanita bushes. They were safe here; no one could approach without their knowledge, and they could see the entire village below them.

Things became quiet in the house, and in each cubicle a similar scene was being enacted. The old men had their favorite grandsons lying beside them, and mothers had their suckling young. The old men stroked their grandsons while they chewed angelica root, in that way imparting much power to the youngsters, making them sufficiently strong to withstand the power of the supernaturals invoked by the enemies. The youngsters were frightened and tense; they recognized fear when they saw it and fear had been predominant all evening, but gradually the tension slackened. At last only murmurs came from the various cubicles.

The old people were instructing the youngsters about how to behave in the immediate future. They were saying, "You must not go out of the house by yourself; if you must go, ask me to come with you. There will be little to eat—no fish, no meat, no grease. You must behave and not make any trouble—you must be quiet at all times."

When Young Boy asked, "Grandfather, why is Elder Relative so sick?" his answer was:

"Because the Sun-executioners have taken his spirit to the Abode of the Dead in the south. If they keep his spirit there, he will never get well. If the doctors win, then his spirit will come back to his body and he will recover. Or it may be that Gilyak, who flies about and takes people away to the Abode of the Dead in the south, has caused Elder Relative's illness. If Gilyak keeps Elder Relative's spirit then he will die."

"What is death, Grandfather?"

The old man pondered for a moment; was this the right time to talk to the boy of these matters? It might take his mind off the present situation and relieve his anxiety. Settling himself comfortably and leaning on an elbow, he began, "In the early times, nothing was as you see it now.

106

"After Coyote had created people he walked around all over the world and at last came to the eastern end, where there were living a people whom Coyote had created and sent there. He married one of their women and settled down among them. The others were all quite rich, but Coyote himself was very poor and had no possessions. He thought the matter over and decided that he would have to make some of the people sick so that he could doctor them, for he was a great medicine man.

"Pretty soon the chief's wife fell ill and lay there sick for four days. No one knew how to help her, for no one knew what was the matter with her. Finally Coyote told his wife that he knew what was the trouble and that he could cure her, and would do so, for four strings of beads. The chief agreed to this, so Coyote went out and collected eight of the large cocoons from which cocoon rattles are made. He took these from the hazel, the blue blossom and from one other shrub called 'Tsu-kale.' He first removed the pupa from each and then hung them up to dry. Next he secured certain feathers, some of which provided a base for the cocoons, and other, finer feathers were used as trimmings around the edges as a sort of topknot on the rattle. He put small gravel in the cocoons, to make them rattle. Next he obtained some obsidian. Thus prepared, he dressed in a full medicine man's costume and went to doctor the woman.

"He came into the chief's house singing and shaking his rattle, and found the woman lying on the floor with her head toward the east. At her head her relatives had placed a pole about five feet tall from which hung the beads. He sat beside her bed and sang special chants for a long time. Then he went out. He did this each morning and evening for four days. On the last day he took her down to the river and sat her down on the bank. Then he dipped his topknot into the water and sprinkled her all over with it four times, after which she was completely cured.

"No one had ever been sick before. That is how Coyote created sickness."

"But sometimes people are hurt and get blood on them," said the boy.

"Yes, that's so," said the old man, "and there is another story about that kind of sickness. Coyote decided that since so many of the others were well off, he would create something else that

107

could do them harm; so he created grizzly bear and sent him out into the brush. Soon after that the hunters went out to set their snares for deer. They set many snares and then went into the brush and made a great noise in order to drive the deer out and into the runways where the snares were set. They caught several deer, and in one of the nets they saw the grizzly, who acted as though he had been caught in it. Of course the hunters did not know what the bear was, for there never had been any such animal until Coyote created him. They came up close to the snare thinking to kill the creature; instead he attacked the men and killed one of them. The rest ran away to wait until the bear had gone. Then they went back, made a stretcher, and carried the hunter's body back to the village, where everyone wailed and mourned his death.

"From the east and from the west, may the Daylight Ducks come quickly and bring the daylight soon.

"That is the way that death began."

In the next cubicle another old man was warning his grandson about carelessness. "I shall tell you of something that happened a long time ago to a young man and his wife in the foothills. The man ran ahead of his wife and said to her in a joking way, 'Try to shoot me.' The woman did so and her arrow killed her husband. That accident started great trouble between the two families, because the man's mother then said that the woman's parents had told her to kill the man. The wife lived with her mother-in-law for two or three months, during which time she and the other relatives poisoned her until she died. You must never make mock of serious things.

"When the man said, 'Try to shoot me,' the supernatural pointed the arrow toward him. You must never do such things, for even if you don't mean to do wrong, to hurt another, or to cause misfortune, someone will say that you did, and they may try to poison you."

Elder Relative had fallen asleep soon after the return of Head Man and his party, but he had tossed and cried out in his sleep and awakened in a state of terror. His dreams had been confused, but simply to have dreamed was dangerous. He had a sensation of being lifted and carried away, and had fought until two of the men nearby could not control him. The entire household had been awakened by his cries: the women had started to wail and the children to cry. Head Man chanted and prayed while he massaged the patient. Finally Elder Relative quieted and fell into a half-conscious state.

The night passed. As the first light appeared in the east the sentry entered the door and awakened the Head Man, for when a member of a household was sick the entire family arose earlier than usual. The guards were left on duty while the rest of the household went down to the river for their morning bath. The morning baths had an almost ritual character; they were indulged in not only for physical cleanliness, but to eradicate any possible traces of poison. When they returned, the guards were relieved and took their baths also.

The light meal of mush was eaten, the house put in order, and all received their instructions for the day. As soon as it was light, Head Man said to some of the men, "You search outside the house." To others he said, "You search the ground and the brush."

One group went into the brush approximately a hundred yards from the house and began a systematic search, scrutinizing every inch of the ground. The other group carefully searched the sides and top of the house. Suddenly one man said, excitedly, "I see something! Two of you, lift me up."

When they had, he reached out with his left hand and plucked something from the grass of the roof. The object was a small arrow, which they all knew immediately was made of poison oak. When a household contained a sick man an enemy would go into the hills, make a bow and arrow of poison oak while singing the proper prayers and curses, and then shoot the arrow onto the roof of the house. He could shoot the arrow over the house into the brush so that it would be harder to find, but it was more potent if it fell on the roof, and would hasten the sick man's death.

As they were examining the arrow, the Head Man came over and took it from them, using his left hand, as always.

In a little while another man came in from the brush, bearing a rabbit.

The Head Man was worried, for the rabbit was fresh-killed and had been hung in the brush so that its shadow would point toward the sick man in the house. The taboo on fresh meat had thus been broken, and the danger was great. The news of Elder Relative's illness must of course have been known by everyone by the time the doctors had arrived; enemies were quick to act. It was the arrow that worried him the most however since it might have been shot toward the house some time ago. The lizard he had found had been buried for at least twenty-four hours. It was a bad sign that so much had happened in so short a time, and it only made matters worse that Elder Relative's wife happened to be pregnant.

He told the sentries to remain on duty, called the three men who had been with him the previous night, and started toward the hills. They would have to redirect the poison towards the poisoner and away from Elder Relative and the rest of the family. The power that was at work had to be guided into a different direction.

The Head Man wanted to remain until the doctor and his assistants arrived, but the longer he delayed, the more power would be extracted from Elder Relative by the supernaturals.

When they arrived at the same site they had visited the previous night, they performed almost the same rituals. When they had completed their work they rubbed themselves with angelica root, went down to the stream, and washed themselves to remove all traces of contamination; to do so in cold water was of the utmost importance. Then they returned to the village. Their life continued in its usual course, but everyone seemed to be keeping away from the sick man's house; everyone was aware that the doctor and his assistants were continuing their attempts at cure.

It was night again. Man of Many Beads stood in the shadow. Sentry duty was tiresome, but at the same time exciting. He felt almost invisible, blending as he did with the shadows around the house. He was relaxed yet alert and ready for instant action. His eyes constantly searched all about. Everything was quiet; more than an hour had passed and he could feel stiffness creeping into his muscles, and craved some action for relief. He had been chosen for sentry duty because, as an excellent deer hunter, he was accustomed to assume one position and remain unmoving for long periods of time.

As he peered in all directions his thoughts kept turning to Long Haired Woman. He made himself stop every time he began thinking of sex, for it meant danger to the entire family to do so at this time; but he couldn't help himself, and this frightened him. Everyone said that it was bad and dangerous to think of sex at a time like this, or when hunting deer, or while on a war party, or in other such situations. Then he began to wonder how long it would be before he could go to Long Haired Woman, now that Elder Relative was sick. If Elder Relative were poisoned, it might be a long time. Head Man, he knew, thought that matters had so far been taken care of very well, but that if anything more happened the family would continue to be in danger.

Elder Relative had seemed fine today. The doctors had indeed helped him. The old men had indicated that they expected Elder Relative to be well by the end of the four-day cure. If that were so, he would be able to see Long Haired Woman and sleep with her.

"It's good," he thought, "that we have so many affiliations with Long Haired Woman's family. Despite my trouble, my family does not suspect them of wanting to harm us. I have my own children with Long Haired Woman, and my mother's brother's children besides." His mother's brother's children ranged in age from some who were older than Man of Many Beads to some who were younger. The men who were older than Man of Many Beads and were married lived with their wives in different households; he had little to do with them.

None had remarked about his eyebrows—they had far more important matters on their minds. For this he was grateful, although he would have preferred to attract everyone's attention rather than endure the present situation and being kept from resolving his difficulties with Long Haired Woman.

Suddenly he saw a shadow detach itself from the dark night and move close to the house. He let fly an arrow. Almost simultaneously with the twang of the bow and the whish of the arrow there was a cry and the shadow began to run rapidly toward the

111

brush. He knew that he had hit the man. His second arrow followed the first almost immediately. By this time there was a commotion within the house; he ran in the direction in which the shadow had fled. He searched all about, but could not find anyone. Others joined in the search, but the enemy had vanished. Troubled, the men returned to the house.

Chapter XI

LONG Haired Woman had been told of Elder Relative's illness. She was sorry now that she had gone to bed with her grandmother. For now she would not be able to see Man of Many Beads for some time; certainly they would not be able to have any intimate relations until after Elder Relative was well again. She knew of cases in which, as a result of illness and then a death, and then another illness, and activities such as hunting, fishing, or gambling, a man and wife had not had intercourse for as long as a year. She also knew of cases where the taboo had been broken and had resulted in misfortune and death. Despite the knowledge that supernaturals were involved, she resented the necessity of refraining from intimacies at those times. At times she herself had broken taboos and nothing untoward had happened. But she also knew that taboo-breaking could lead to sickness. Then the doctor, by questioning, would diagnose the illness as due to carelessness or ignorance, or to the lack of regard of the taboos. Then the entire family would resent the wantonness that resulted in troubles for the entire family.

She thought about herself and Man of Many Beads and grew worried, but she knew she had no one to blame but herself. On the other hand, she had to make Man of Many Beads realize that, although she loved him, she could not accept his philandering. She hoped that Elder Relative would become well soon, that he was ghost-sick or that his illness was due to a broken taboo, but not to poisoning. She was glad that Man of Many Beads had returned to her the first night. Her being with her grandmother at the time was not an additional shame to him. Men often remained in the sweathouse all night, and at such times the older women generally kept the young females at their sides. She loved Man of Many Beads and was glad that they had children; if they hadn't had children his family would certainly suspect her of having poisoned Elder Relative.

She thought back to how they had met and married. As a young man, Man of Many Beads had been chosen by his mother's brother to be trained in gambling. Thus Man of Many Beads had been with him a great deal. That uncle had been married to Long Haired Woman's father's sister. When he had died, Man of Many Beads, as was customary, had married his widow, an old woman with many children. Thus Man of Many Beads was the legal father of children, some of them older than himself. Before that marriage, Man of Many Beads and Long Haired Woman had often noticed each other, and they had had an unspoken understanding that their attraction would culminate in marriage. At the proper time, therefore, a secondary marriage ceremony had been performed. It was *lamatch*—a small ceremony, very different from the marriage ceremony for a boy and girl neither of whom had been married previously. It had been a real love affair, although it was also a traditional means of continuing a family in the event of the death of a married person with children. The families involved always endeavored to bind their relationship more securely. When a man married a woman, they endeavored, whenever possible, to have the man's younger brother marry the woman's younger sister. In the case of the death of either the man or the woman, the survivor took over both families. They went even further in encouraging the marriage of a husband's sister to the wife's brother. In some families the marriages had been going on generation after generation for so long that a marriage rarely occurred outside the long-established relationship. These families never had to worry about poison from each other, and outsiders were afraid to get involved in a feud with any member of either family, for fear of having so large and powerful a group to contend with.

These marriages occurred for another reason. Since a man went to live with his wife at her home, the married male members of the family were strangers to that family. To have a number of males living in one household promised support and security. Furthermore, there was a good possibility that one of them would eventually become the Head Man of the family. There was a conflict involved in deciding whether to have the males marry into different families in order to build up a great number of affiliations, or try to get as many as possible into one family to insure a stronger and thus more reliable ally.

Long Haired Woman thought of her husband as he had been when he had returned from the last deer hunt and she had been so proud of his prowess and prestige.

He had prepared himself carefully for the deer hunt. He and his two older relatives had fasted, made their preparations and their prayers; had gone into the hills taking their deerhead masquerade from its hiding place, had sung, danced and prayed over it. The oldest man had massaged and rubbed Man of Many Beads with angelica to give him more power. The change in weather had been to the good, and they had shot two deer immediately. When they brought them back, each had taken some of the meat to his own home, and left the rest at the Chief's house.

The Chief had announced the bounty to the village, and the heads of families had come individually for their share. They placed a string of beads on the blanket before the house and picked up a cut of meat that seemed proportionate to their payment; no one made note of how much money they had left in exchange for the meat. When all the meat except a choice piece had been taken no more men appeared. The Chief tied the strings of beads together; he saw that there was more than enough money, took the surplus for himself as well as the last piece of venison; this he gave to the head woman of his house. Then he sent a messenger for the oldest deer hunter, and gave him the money he had collected.

Chapter XII

THE old man on sentry duty in the hills settled himself comfortably and said to his grandson, "Last night you asked me about matters which men do not discuss in the home. I was going to answer your question briefly, but what's happened to Elder Relative makes it necessary to have a long talk with you. I've already told you about sickness and poison. Now I'll try to fill out your knowledge of the most important matters of our lives. Up to now you've learned only the broad general things that all boys and girls must know.

"Now that Elder Relative has been stricken we shall have to expect all kinds of trouble and you are old enough at fifteen, and have received enough power from me, to be an active member of the famiy. It's clear now, isn't it, that danger surrounds us at all times? At first we all thought that Elder Relative had only encountered a ghost, then the doctor found out that it was a supernatural, and that it happened because his wife is pregnant. But now, in addition, we've found the lizard, the poison arrow, and the fresh-killed rabbit; so we know that his sickness is also the result of poisoning. What we've found shows that our enemies have added more poison during the last few days. Elder Relative has little power left, and that means the whole family is less powerful. Every enemy of ours will now try to harm us all, and especially Elder Relative because his weakness makes it easier to kill him.

"There are so many different kinds of poison and so many sources of it that it is difficult for the doctor to determine exactly which cure must be instituted. It may take a lot of time to find out whether a professional poison man is behind the sickness or just some common man. And there are many other complications."

The boy looked puzzled, and the old man tried to make himself clearer.

"It's like this—every family is involved in one or more feuds. The young people are only told that they are not allowed to play with or go near the members of certain families. It is not until the older people in the family feel that a youngster must know more in order to protect himself, or has accumulated enough power, that they inform him of all the details.

"When a family has enemies—as all families do—it means that every member of that family is an enemy to every member of the other family from the youngest to the eldest. Feuds have been going on between some families for as long as anyone can remember; no one knows how they began. Right now our family has feuds going on with three families. It costs a lot of money, but we must spend it in order to protect ourselves. Only after we can kill them off will we be safe.

"Feuds can begin in many ways. One started because a man put his hand on a woman during a Big-Time. A few days later the skin where he had touched her cracked and she became very sick. That showed that he had poisoned her. In another case, a man offered a woman three thousand beads for a basket that was worth fifteen thousand. She had to sell it because she needed the money very badly. He later found out that she was talking about him. Since that meant that her family would poison him, he started to poison her first. When she became sick her family initiated poisoning him. Ever since the deaths of those two, the families have gone on poisoning each other."

"What kind of poison did they use?"

"Well, there are many professional poison men, as you know. Each has his own kind of poison, and only that one kind, and his assistants know only the same kind. They can make that poison out of almost anything; doctors use anything they can that's out of the ordinary and peculiar. They use the feathers of the California road runner, yellow jacket, spider, and red ant stings; a slab from a poison rock, various herbs, blossoms, beeswax, frogs, rattlesnakes, mountain lizards, red belly snakes, copperheads, and bull snake eggs, and two-headed snakes—these are the most dangerous. Snakes, lizards, and turtles are cut open and held over a fire, and the blood and grease drippings caught. Combinations of these various ingredients are pounded together in a mortar and made into a paste. Some doctors then put some on a forked stick and let a rattlesnake strike it. While they are preparing the poison they pray and sing and dance constantly; they never stop, except at night, and all this goes on for four days.

"During this period the doctors only drink water before sunrise and eat a little mush after sunset, and nothing else at all during the day. Every night when they have finished their work they put the mixture in a hollow rock. Then they take off the costumes they have been wearing and hide them in a secret place in the hills. When they come back to work their poison every morning, they put them on again; meanwhile they sing and chant and pray, wearing special gloves to protect themselves. They always take the ingredients or mixture with their left hand first before putting it in their right hand, as we always do when someone shows us something new. They have to be especially careful, for if they made one mistake, they would kill themselves instead of the person they are poisoning.

"When they think the poison is just about right they test it by applying it to a deerskin; it makes the skin shrink. They're very careful not to make the poison too powerful for fear of its making them weak, and therefore sick; so the poison is always a little weak at the first test. They test it three more times, each time using a new skin. When the skin shrinks up very tight they know the mixture is ready.

"Sometimes these poison men manufacture poison, selling it to others for their personal use. It's sometimes hard to catch the poison men because when they leave the hills they each go in a different direction and enter the village from different sides, each carrying some poison with him. If one of them meets a friend, or close relative, or his *awihinawa*, who would ordinarily touch him, he just says, 'Don't touch me; I am fixed for gambling.'

"Often poison men make a special brew to kill a specific

person. Someone might get hold of your toe or fingernail parings, or your urine or other excretions, or hair or semen, or some piece of your clothing, and give it to the poison man. He can do many bad things, given such substances. Sometimes men don't take these things to the poison doctors, but use them themselves. That's cheap poison, and not so dangerous. They perform all kinds of rituals with what they've managed to get, praying for what they want and doing their best to make you sick.

"Then there is the power woman who doesn't have to get hold of anything; she can do harm just by praying and wishing; she is very dangerous and has much power, but there are very few such women and no one ever knows who they are.

"This is why mothers are so careful about their children. When they change the moss from between an infant's legs, they don't throw it away, but bury it. And that's why young children are always accompanied when they go into the bush to take care of nature's needs. A poison man or an enemy can pick up your dung with a split stick. That's why you must always cover up your spit or dung or urine with dirt or ashes. It's enough for someone to smear your dung, for instance, on a piece of poison oak and put it under your house for you to be in danger. Even if someone gets hold of your real name, they can poison you; that's why we never tell people our real names.

"Sometimes poison is worked by making a figure out of a forked stick of poison oak. A little oak ball is put on for the head, with beads used for the eyes and other bits for a mouth, nose, and ears. Pitch is put on top of the head, and some hair stolen from the person to be poisoned is stuck on top. Then the spit, urine, nail parings, dung, or anything else of the victim's is rubbed over the figure. Semen is always the strongest thing to use for a man. Then the poisoner takes some of the mixture bought from the poison doctor and rubs this over the figure too, and while he's doing so calls the figure by the real name of the victim. Then he says, 'So-and-So is getting sick,' and 'So-and-So is dying.' Then he makes a little bed of grass and places the image upon it, and he and his relatives gather around the bed, just as if they were gathering around the bed of a dying man. They cry and shed tears and wail, and act exactly as if there were a real man lying there. After that they cremate the figure, to make certain that the victim will not be able to come back to the body. The intended victim dies—unless he gets the services of a powerful doctor who can stop this poisoning because this is very strong poison.

"But sometimes your enemies don't want to kill you, only make you suffer. That isn't strong poison, but it is bad just the same. A man gets a rattlesnake when it is shedding its skin and therefore blind. He takes its eyes, grinds them up, and spreads them on an abalone shell, which he then flashes towards his victim, meanwhile praying that he or she become as blind as the snake.

"It is possible to get a doctor to cause someone to be sick for a long time, so that the family will spend a lot of money, but not to kill the person. We did that once; the man was sick for three years. But the other family had a good doctor, and our poison doctor had to make his medicine stronger all the time. In the end the man died. But that may have been because someone else put fresh meat near the house, or shot an arrow into the house, or things like that.

"But those doctors are not good people; you can't trust them. Some of them are just money-makers. They can give you *yɔ'ba:sa.*

"If business is slack a doctor can visit a healthy man and recommend his own talents. 'I'm a good doctor,' he will say. 'You'd better try me out the next time you get sick.' Within a day or two the man will start to feel drowsy and tired and exhausted. He feels all right while the sun is up but very sick when the sun goes down. The man knows that he is *yɔ'ba:sa.* The only cure is to hire the same doctor to work his magic. If he doesn't get the same doctor the victim usually goes crazy and dies. The doctor gives *yɔ'ba:sa* by rubbing his hand with a power stone and touching his victim secretly.

"There are other ways, too, of poisoning someone. If you get some part of a man, like dung, and place it on a grave, and wish your enemy to go to his death in the same way that the corpse did, that man will die. Or you can take it and throw it into any body of water, and wish for Bagil to take the person.

"There is a secret pond in our territory called *kɔmka;* if any bit of an individual is thrown into it, he dies. Even so small a

121

thing as a hair or nail paring will cause certain death. Hair will make a person crazy first, and bring on death within a month. Moccasins or a toenail paring will make a person start to die from the feet up. Fingernail parings will cause the arms to go first."

The boy's face showed great interest. He asked, "Can anyone do that? Can you?"

"No. If a common person should throw something into *k'ɔmka,* nothing happens. But common people are afraid to go near that lake anyway. One must have the right power songs. If you don't, you hire a poison doctor to do it for you. I've only once seen that lake myself. There are all kinds of Indian beads, Indian gold, baskets, pieces of clothing, and other things—oh, a great deal of wealth in it."

"Ai," said the boy, "one could get rich easily."

"No," exclaimed the Old Man. "I would not touch any of those things for fear of getting sick and dying. No one but a poison man will go near that place. When he throws the object in, he also throws money in along with it. All the while he keeps praying and chanting. He says, 'Here is what you wanted; take it, and take the person who belongs to it.'"

The old man saw that Youngster wanted to ask a question, and nodded his permission. Youngster asked, "Isn't it possible to do something to those doctors and poison men and enemies without hiring someone to do it for you?"

"Yes," said the old man, "that is why we are sitting here. I am watching to see if anyone is going to the hills or coming back. A poison doctor can take from five to seven days to collect his ingredients, build his fire, and make his paste. He keeps sending his assistants to find specific ingredients, and as I told you, they all come back every night. We killed one of them— the one we saw fix the deerskin. After he left that night, we killed six birds and six rabbits. Then we built a big fire where the doctor had had his fire, and burned all the animals. The doctor became ill that very night and died the next morning. That's a sure way for anybody to kill a doctor. If we had only found one rabbit, we would have burned only the rabbit blood, and then it would take longer for the doctor to die.

"Those poison doctors are bad. They use all kinds of dangerous things that we are afraid to touch. For instance, they try to get hold of some ashes after a cremation—a small sprinkle of those ashes in someone's food means quick death. Or sometimes in the sweathouse they can sift a few ashes on a sleeping man's lips. Then when the man licks his lips he gets poisoned and dies. Or they get a piece of bone from a cremated person, which is just as powerful, and put that where it will kill you.

"Sometimes people are poisoned when a small object is thrown at them—a small piece of earth, a pebble, or something like that, but this is done only to the dancers or men who take care of a dance outfit. One old man who was the caretaker of a dance outfit became very sick that way. Doctors were called in, but could do nothing for him. A little screech owl was around this man constantly, chattering and making noises, but no one knew what it wanted. After the old man died, the people found some green pepper wood nuts under his bed. That only works with caretakers, though.

"Sometimes, when a person knows his victim's real name, he makes a figure of the victim out of wood, brush, and grass, and then shoots the image with a bow and arrow, chanting and praying and cursing. He says, 'I am going to shoot you. I am going to shoot you.' He keeps saying the man's name. Then he shoots him, and he says, 'You are shot; you are dying.' And the victim gets sick and dies. Oh, there are many ways of harming people. People make powder out of snake eyes and rattles and other parts of the body, stand so the wind is blowing toward the victim, and let the powder fly toward the man and blind him. Do you remember what I told you about the abalone shell? Some people do it one way; some another."

During his recital, the old man's gaze moved constantly over the village. He watched various individuals move into the brush, toward the streams, and toward the hills. Youngster did the same. They saw the Chief come out of his house, stroll through the village, stop occasionally and speak to different people.

"Grandfather, isn't it possible for the Chief to do something to stop all this poisoning?"

"The Chief can do very little by himself; he is only able to do what the people want. He does preach to us to be good to one another, and he can stop a brawl, as you saw. But he's in a very difficult position. He has the greatest honor and prestige, and makes all intertribal decisions during the council of the Chiefs. We always back him up then. But he's careful to follow the wish of the people and not to do as he pleases. Since he dare not make mistakes, he very seldom does anything except talk and tell us to be good to one another, not to growl or make trouble.

"He is the one who announces everything that happens or is going to happen, after he himself has been informed. It's he who announces such occasions as a Big-Time, a group deer hunt, fishing party, quail hunt, and so on. Although he presides at a council meeting, ordinarily there is very little for him to do.

"Once in a great while a Head Man will ask the Chief to intercede in some trouble. There have been only a few cases in which he has been asked to stop a poisoning feud, and then it is not known by everyone. We keep that information from him; we don't want him to know when we are poisoning people. We want him to think highly of us."

"But," asked Youngster reasonably, "if he doesn't have much power, why do you want him to think highly of you?"

"It's very important to have him think your family good since he distributes the catch after a group fishing party, quail drive, or deer hunt, and it's he who decides how much—or little—food you'll get. He also distributes money and presents that he has received from a visiting tribe. And when a deer hunter brings the meat to the chief to sell for him, if he's a good man from a good family, the Chief will give him more money."

"Why is it the Chief who distributes the food or money?" asked the boy. "Why doesn't the hunter sell the meat to whoever will pay the highest price?"

"Because the Chief would never poison anyone and his power is such that the power is removed from any object he touches. For that reason no one ever gives the Chief anything he has poisoned. Furthermore, the Chief always intermingles all the money so that if anyone were trying to poison a certain individual he would be unsuccessful; what's more, the item might be given to a relative of the poisoner himself. This is also true for visiting tribes. Large amounts of money and other valuables are handed over by the Chief of the visiting tribe to ours, and if our Chief were to get sick and die, we'd know the other tribe was responsible."

"But, Grandfather, how does a man become a Chief?"

"In the same way a person becomes the Head Man in a family, and the way men become fishermen, hunters, gamblers, poison men, doctors, money makers, arrow and spearhead makers, or any other professional. It's most important for a Chief or a Head Man to be a good talker, to be calm, just, and strong and never envious. The Chief and his assistants always keep an eye on their young male relatives from the time they're born. In a big family—and the Chief's family is always the largest—there are many professions, and the important men in these professions always observe the young people. They're good to the young boys, give them presents, spend time with them, instruct them. As time goes on, the boys show special interest and ability in certain activities. If a boy shows greatest interest and ability in fishing, for instance, the fishermen spend more and more time with him. In the case of a Head Man or the Chief, when they think a young boy has shown special chiefly abilities, they start to work on him—they counsel him, they favor him, they transmit power to him. Most important of all, they start teaching him all the languages of all the different peoples with whom we have contact, as well as the special language that all Chiefs and their male and female assistants know.

"The boy they pick can be any young male relative. Sometimes it is the Chief's younger brother. As you know a man can have a brother who is forty years younger than he is because a man can marry a woman and have children and if his wife dies, marry another woman and have children by her. His widow can marry one of his relatives, and they can have children. This can go on and on, and has, in many families, as you know. A man you call Elder Brother can be as old as your grandfather, and a man you call Younger Brother can be younger than your great grandson.

"Since the chief's family is larger than our own, there are usually many more young men in it. When a young man is chosen to learn how to be trained to be a Chief, he must be very careful in his sex-life. He must never mate with anyone

125

not his wife, for fear of hurting the position of the Chief and his assistants. For this reason Chiefs have more than one wife, all of whom are his assistants and help him when tribes get together. They too are carefully chosen from the most important families of our tribe. This is another way in which the Chief accumulates power, for he then has the most important and strongest families to support him.

"All of our people, all the families, always give the Chief presents—they bring him baskets, meat, fish, money. He needs all these things because he is the one who must feed and entertain messengers and visitors from other tribes and give presents to other Chiefs. He must be wealthy so that he can help out poor families and encourage depressed ones.

"So there is always a number of men from whom the next Chief will be chosen, when this one dies. The people don't simply choose the next oldest man; they choose the particular one they think has the best qualifications. The whole tribe discusses it. The men in each family decide the matter and when they are agreed they inform their Head Man, who considers the choice with the other Head Men; when they are all agreed they have a council meeting, at which they appoint the new Chief. But we don't wait for a Chief to die; that only happens by accident or in war. The usual way is for an aging Chief to let it be known that it's time for someone to take his place. Then he acts as an advisor to the new one. That isn't what happens in the professions, however; in those cases the oldest survivor becomes the head and the director.

"Because the Chief's family is so powerful, the other families always try to become related to him, but the Chief's family is very careful in their choices.

"You can see that the Chief has a great deal of power, but can't do very much by himself. In our case we don't know who is poisoning Elder Relative, nor why. We have our feuds, as I said, but we wouldn't want to let the Chief know that we have used poison; so we cannot go to him and he can do nothing for us.

"Elder Relative doesn't seem to be dangerously sick. If he had gone to bed because he felt sick or tired, or if he had vomited, or his skin had cracked or he couldn't move his legs or arms or had a bad pain somewhere in his body, we'd know that he had been poisoned directly, and by a professional poison man. But it looks as if some cheap poison has been used, and he has enough power to resist it."

"Are there different kinds of poison then, grandfather?"

"Yes, there are. There is *tↄ'se*, which is put in food or drink. With this kind of poison the victim coughs a great deal, his lungs dry up, and he dies. Then there is *ka'ↄ*, which is rattlesnake and other oils mixed together into a paste. Then there is *baxↄbaxↄ*. Anyone poisoned with that will have all his skin eaten off his bones and always dies. There can be another poison added to *ka'ↄ*, that results in paralysis. Such poisons are also called *komshil*, and direct contact is necessary. A poison man can touch you with his finger or cane, or he can take hold of your arm in a friendly fashion.

"Once I saw a woman dancer performing during a Big-Time. A man stepped up and took hold of her arm to lead her to another side of the fire. Later on she became very sick, her arm swelled badly, and the poison traveled through her body. By the time she died, she had also been stricken with insanity.

"Another time I saw a man trying to make love to a woman. He put his arms around her waist from behind and put his hands on her stomach. The woman did not care for him and pushed him away. Some time later her flesh cracked around the vicinity of her navel. Many doctors worked on her and tried to save her, but they all failed.

"These poison men, or anyone else who is trying to poison you, get close to you so they can touch you with the poison, or get you to touch some article that they've touched with the paste—an article of clothing, your blanket, or anything else of yours. Any way they do it works, as long as there is contact. You usually die in six moons or a year from this kind of poison. Sometimes they sneak around, especially at a big dance, and touch ycu with their hand or a stick. Sometimes they have a dance just to be able to get hold of a certain man or his family. A lot of this is done in the sweathouse too. Someone can put the poison on a rock, heat it, and then sear you with it—that works very quickly and it's very bad.

"So you can never be too careful. You must always watch

out for these poison doctors. We know who they are, which is why we are afraid when a doctor pays us a visit. Often it means that someone in the family will get sick. If he wants to buy a basket or something else cheap, we sell it, because it costs more to get him to treat you. Oh, it's all very complicated. There are poison men, the snake oil men, the men who go up to the mountains and throw stuff in the pond, the power women, the common enemies. The common man is easier to catch. It is hard work for him, and it sometimes takes him six moons or longer because he doesn't have enough knowledge or power. He must wait until certain blossoms and other things are ripe in order to make his poison, and all the time he does that he isn't able to eat meat or fish or grease.

"We don't do that; it's better and quicker to get a poison man."

"How do you know which poison man to get?"

"You pick the man who uses the methods and the kind of poisons you favor. If you want your enemy to die slowly, in much pain, and so that it costs him a lot of money, you pick one particular poisoner; if you want him to die fast, you pick another. Sometimes you get two or more different poison men unknown to one another to work on the same victim simultaneously. That's the best way. The victim dies fast then, but it costs a lot of money. But poison men can always trick you, and everyone is afraid of that, which is why some people just buy the poison and use it themselves. We have a strong poison man in our family, which saves us money and protects us because we know that the other family can't pay him to poison us. Sometimes you pay a poison man to do some harm to your enemy, and your enemy finds out and pays the poison man more than you did to do you harm instead."

"Can poison men cure you too?"

"Yes, they can. But there are the sucking doctors, who only cure you, and never poison you. A sucking doctor can see a light flashing in front of a sick man's head that no one else can see. When the sucking doctor cures a patient he then becomes a sucking doctor himself. He goes all over the territory, visiting other tribes, sucking the poison out of people, whether it be in the form of a worm, blood, or an unusual object, like a peculiar stone. He massages you too, and sings songs of his own. He is different.

"The Kuksu doctor, like the one we have, also only cures his own people. It is only when one tribes poisons another that he and his assistants go to work."

"Will you tell me some stories about how we learned to poison and cure people, grandfather?"

"Yes, I shall, if all is well. But let's go home now. It's so dark that we can't see anyone coming from the hills anyway."

Youngster had already sensed much of what his grandfather had told him, but now that he knew more of the details he felt fearful and apprehensive.

The old man regretted that he had to instruct the youth earlier than was customary. Usually such matters were taught to a boy over a longer period. But the boy had to be prepared. A youngster known to be a virgin, who was level-headed, fearless and dependable, and uncontaminated by various powers, was always chosen as the instrument by means of which power was directed and controlled. In these unusual cases maturation was speeded up. Sometimes the knowledge of five, ten or as in this case, fifteen years, had to be transmitted in one sitting. This was also true of gambling. When gamblers were ready to wager a huge sum, they would choose a young apprentice to do the actual physical gambling for them, meanwhile sitting behind him, warding off evil power by their physical presence, and constantly chanting and praying and transmitting their power to him. In that way their power would invalidate the power of the opponent, and the young gambler would win.

Chapter XIII

IT was night again. The men had finished the evening meal and were gradually filling the sweathouse. The gambling and conversations had started.

Elder Relative was now well, and it was many days since Man of Many Beads had been shamed and separated from Long Haired Woman. He was in a quandary, for he did not like giving in, and he knew she couldn't come to him at his mother's house, not only because it was not proper, but because he had no cubicle of his own there. He wasn't eager to have their relatives effect a reconciliation either. He wanted her to understand that she couldn't rule him. It was sufficient that she had plucked his face clean and shamed him publicly; she did not have to go to bed with her grandmother. Yet, she might have been right since she had no way of knowing whether he would return the same night. "But I came back to her right away," he thought, "and maybe I should go back tonight. No, let her wait. She should let me know that she is sorry." But still he was dissatisfied. He could not enter into the discussions going on about him although he vaguely heard snatches of conversation. His mind kept wandering to his personal difficulties and his desire for his wife. Finally he stood up, left the sweathouse, and went to his wife's house and their own cubicle.

Long Haired Woman appeared to be asleep. He carefully insinuated himself under the blanket and pressed close to her. At first she was rigid, but as his hands moved over her warm body, she relaxed and pressed close to him. It was clear that she welcomed this opportunity for reconciliation; otherwise she would have rejected him roughly.

They were both happy that the trouble was over and that she had forgiven him. Conferences between the two families would have been troublesome and awkward; now it would all be forgotten very soon.

They fell asleep peacefully.

The old woman was happy too, having seen Man of Many Beads enter the house and get into bed with his wife. He was a good son-in-law, a deer hunter who brought much home, a gambler who won regularly; he came from a powerful family who could be relied upon in times of trouble; and he was agreeable when it came to making vital decisions. Now there would be no need for coldness between the two families. Shaming Man of Many Beads had been a good way of taking care of the matter. His people knew that Long Haired Woman had been counseled not to do anything more drastic, and they must have been pleased to have had the matter resolved in so short a time. If Man of Many Beads wanted another woman, he might be able to get Long Haired Woman's younger sister, in which case there would be no trouble. Perhaps it could be arranged without too much difficulty.

Wakim and Kabemok had met a number of times during the past month, but each time they had been careful, so that when the day of her month-sick arrived without blood flow Kabemok was not overly worried; sometimes there was a day's delay. But when the next day passed and she didn't even have any pains she began to worry. All during the night she twisted and turned in anxiety.

Now that it was too late, she was sorry that she hadn't taken the mistletoe brew. Perhaps she could jump off high rocks, lift very heavy burdens, work especially hard, or hit her stomach— or maybe she could wear a baby-squeeze. That would do it, but whom could she get to make one for her who had enough power and a knowledge of the songs? One would have to dry the bark of the right kind of tree in a certain way, roll it between the palms, shred it into threads, and then weave it in a prescribed way, and then it had to be prayed to properly. She had seen one of those belts—they were finely woven, even more so than a basket, three eighths of an inch thick and one and a half inches wide. It had to be drawn so tight that breathing would be very difficult. Of course it would be extremely uncomfortable and painful to wear. There were too many difficulties to be overcome there; some other solution would have to be found. And any of them might fail, or even if they worked, she might be found out.

Even if it were successful, and sometimes it took more than a month, there would be other problems. The afterbirth had to be buried, and she would have to be cured by sweating and massage. Girls had omitted these precautions and become very sick as a result, or some even died. One thing or another could go wrong, and sometimes the supernaturals were not taken care of properly. If a married woman used these methods her family and the doctor took care of her. She decided there was a better way; it had worked for other women and it should work for her.

The next time she planned to meet Wakim she would tell her elder sister, who then would tell their grandmother, and the two of them would catch Wakim and her when they were together. It had to be done soon because two of her older married female relatives, who felt they had had enough children, were waiting for her to be month-sick so they could wear her bloodstained garment, the bloodstains of an unmarried girl being one of the surest means of birth control. Therefore she couldn't even feign month-sick. Ordinarily she would have talked to her grandmother about her problem, but she was afraid the old woman would become angry. She had always been wonderful to her, but in a matter of this kind she would only offer censure. You didn't go to your mother about such things. She was always busy taking care of her own or her sister's young children or doing household chores. A mother only took care of ceremonial matters; her daughters did not bother her and seldom spoke to her about anything important. That was something you learned at an early age, in fact almost from birth, that your mother and all the women she called sister made up a group, all of whom treated you about the same. When you cried from hunger, any woman would nurse you. If your mother was in the month-sick house, some other woman took care of you, and if you hurt yourself any woman could care for you. The children made up an undifferentiated group to their "mothers" and "fathers." But as you grew older, one woman began to stand out—your "grandmother"—and you two became close. The tie with your own blood mother might not be very strong, but another tie existed, the one with an older sister, who was like a "little mother" to you. She was closer in age and experience to you, helped you out, and taught you things you were not supposed to know and which your grandmother expected to teach you at a later time. The "little mother" was involved in everything you did, and was the only person to use as a go-between for you and the old woman.

Each person had many elder sisters since female cousins on both father's and mother's side, as well as other relatives, were called by the term "sister." Those who were born before you were elder sister; those born after you younger sister, but there was always one who was the special older sister to you, as you were the special younger sister to her.

She approached her elder sister therefore and said, "Will you walk with me?"

Elder Sister agreed and put away the basket she was working on, and the two left the house.

Kabemok was anxious for everything to go well because, as her father's sister had died less than a year ago, her children needed a mother, and their father, Rock Man, a wife. She had noticed them looking at her. She was the right age, but he was old, and Kabemok did not want to become his wife.

After they had walked some distance, chatting casually, Kabemok said, "You know Wakim? He's a nice man, and I like him."

"Yes, he is nice," said Elder Sister. "But what makes you speak of him? Is he the reason for our walk?"

"It is," said Kabemok. "We've been seeing each other for a long time," she burst out nervously. "Now it is time for my month-sick and nothing has happened."

"Oh, that's bad—there'll be trouble." Elder Sister's voice indicated her distress. As usual it would be too late to do anything except patch things up. She had no real authority; all she could do was advise and help. It was not even proper for her to censure Kabemok. She said only, "What are you going to do? Have you thought of the different ways to take care of it?"

"I don't like any of them."

Elder Sister could not help reproaching her. "I have always told you to wait and never let any man touch you before you are married. But now this has happened, and we mustn't shame the family. What do you want to do?"

"Wouldn't it be best if you and Grandmother found Wakim and me in the bushes tonight?" asked Kabemok.

"That's one way," replied Elder Sister. "But if we do catch you, there are two things we can do. We can get angry and threaten Wakim and make everything public—that's not a good way, and it would cause greater trouble. The other way is for us to find you, become angry, and then leave you two alone to make your decision. That would be best because then Wakim can tell his family that he wants to marry you and no one else need know. And there will be better feeling between the two families."

"I think you are right, Elder Sister."

Thus agreed, they turned back to the house.

Elder Sister went in while Kabemok chatted with relatives who were outdoors working on baskets and clothing. In a few minutes, Elder Sister came out and joined the conversation. In a moment she signaled to Kabemok that her grandmother wanted to see her.

No one was in the house but her grandmother, who was sitting beside the fire. "What is this I hear about you?" her grandmother said harshly. "Haven't you been treated right in this house? Haven't you been taught not to do such things? Now you've brought shame on your family. You've done something you'll remember all your days. You have caused us great trouble, and there'll be more trouble to come. I should make you get in bed with one of the older men who's married to one of your female relatives, and then we can tell everyone that you've been married to him. There's old Rock Man, for one, who'd like to have a second wife."

"I don't love Rock Man; he is old, older than my father. What I have done has been done by many others," said Kabemok rebelliously.

"You will not speak like that, Kabemok—you have been headstrong enough. It is true that such things have happened before, but everyone is ashamed when they do happen. It is bad to get a reputation of that kind; it becomes known, and the men talk, and say you're easy. They use love charms and try to get you themselves. Whom else have you been with? How many other men have there been?"

She didn't wait for an answer. "You will do what I say, otherwise I'll get in bed tonight with Rock Man, even though he is my son-in-law and it's taboo to even talk to a son-in-law. Then I'll make you get in bed with us, after which I will leave the bed, and then you two will be married."

Kabemok took fright at her grandmother's words. She knew that she had been wrong to meet with Wakim, and she felt that she had been wrong to tell her grandmother. But it was too late now to do anything without the aid of her family.

"There is only one consolation," said the old woman. "Wakim is not married to another woman although he has been betrothed since infancy. He's also not a relative whom you call brother, father, or son, only a joking relative, so it would be all right to marry him."

Kabemok had kept quiet. Now she said, "There's been no other man; he's the only one, and he loves me."

"Then why have you two been meeting secretly? Why haven't you asked to get married? Men say these things about love, but they don't mean them. We'll have to do our best to get him to marry you. I would make you marry Rock Man, but then Wakim would talk about you, especially if he really loved you, and that in itself would cause trouble between the families. You will have to do what you and Elder Sister talked about. Now you find your mother and tell her I want to talk with her."

The conversation with Kabemok's mother was almost entirely one-sided; grandmother did all the talking. "Now you will be grown up," she ended by saying. "You have not taken care of your daughter, but that's how all the women are. They never mature until after their daughter is married and has a child of her own. Now you will have to learn what steps to take so that the marriage ceremony, if we have one, is done properly. We shall know by tomorrow what is to be, and you must be ready."

It was dark and quiet when Kabemok and Wakim met that night. The girl was nervous but they went through the preliminaries easily. Suddenly Kabemok's grandmother, who had hidden herself, spoke up in a shrill voice, "What are you doing there? You're doing wrong."

Kabemok whispered, "Oh, nothing's happened, nothing's happened," and Wakim started to rise.

"Stay there," ordered the grandmother. "Don't move."

Elder Sister then came over. She had gone around to the other side to intercept Wakim if he tried to leave. Carefully choosing her words, so there would be no indictment, she said, "How long have you two been meeting each other? Why haven't you asked to be married if you want to be together?"

Wakim said, "We have just met."

"Don't say anything," said the grandmother. "If you want to be with Kabemok, you should speak to your relatives. This is no way to act—you must speak to your family immediately.

"Come," she said to Elder Sister, "we'll leave these two for a few minutes."

They drew off about fifteen yards.

"What shall we do?" said Kabemok.

Wakim had been thinking fast; he was in a trap and he knew it. His first reaction was one of fright at the thought of his family's censure, the men's joking, and the unpleasantness of having been forced to marry. Then he thought, "But why not get married? It is about time, and there is nothing else I can do anyway. If I don't speak to my family about it, then Kabemok's family will surely force the marriage, and then it will become public scandal."

He might as well make the best of a bad situation. "Kabemok, it is time we got married," he said. "I shall speak to my family if you are willing."

"Yes, Wakim, I agree with you; it's the best thing for both of us."

"Tell your relatives that I will speak to my family tonight." They parted.

Kabemok joined her elder sister and grandmother.

The three women started back to the house, Grandmother scolding all the way. "As soon as the mourning period is over, Rock Man was going to marry you," she concluded. "Now we have to find another woman for him because we don't want to lose the children, and we'll have to persuade him not to be angry."

Kabemok kept quiet, happy that she would not have to marry Rock Man, since Wakim was the one she wanted. He was good-looking and was going to be an important man some day—a fisherman and a gambler. Grandmother's complaining voice sounded far away and unimportant.

At his own house Wakim went over to the Head Woman and said, "Grandmother, Kabemok's a nice girl, and her family is a nice family. I have noticed her very much."

His grandmother looked keenly at him. "That's true," she said. "She is a fine girl, of good family. They're easy to get along with, and they have many professions."

"Don't you think I am old enough to have a wife?"

"Yes, you are, indeed," said his grandmother. "But you know you have been betrothed from infancy—what about that other girl?"

"She's needed to take the place of her elder sister, who hasn't yet had any children although she has been married for three years," said Wakim.

"That may be true," said the grandmother, "but as far as we know, the understanding has not been changed between the families." She knew there was something more underlying Wakim's story than he had said, but she didn't want to press for information. There were problems connected with every birth, marriage, death, or anything else that might happen in the family. As female head of the family, her duty was to take care of such matters so that there would be the least amount of friction between the families of the betrothed pair. If this were just a request there would be a good deal of preliminary talking to be done, but if on the other hand this were a necessity because Kabemok was pregnant, or because they had been caught together, it would have to be taken care of with more dispatch. From Wakim's expression and air of tension she thought the latter must be true. "How soon are you to get married, according to your way of thinking?"

"Very soon, I hope. So many things can happen to delay a marriage—a death, a birth, a sickness, among others. It can take a couple of years or more, sometimes. Right now it's possible for us to get married. Is it too late for you to talk to Kabemok's relatives tonight?"

The grandmother realized that there was no alternative. She would have to talk to her younger sisters immediately, then to the relatives of Wakim's betrothed, and then to Kabemok's grandmother. She discussed the matter with her sisters, and within a few minutes they went over to the house of Wakim's betrothed. The old woman who was the head of the household asked them to come over to the fire, where they ate the proffered food. There was courtesy conversation about ordinary matters, then Wakim's grandmother said, "How is your granddaughter? And how are your son-in-law and your childless daughter?"

The old grandmother said, "She has not as yet slept with them in their cubicle."

"Don't you think it's time for that?" said Wakim's grandmother.

"Yes, perhaps you're right. How is Wakim these days? Is he not old enough to have a woman of his own?"

"Yes, he is getting old enough and we think perhaps he ought to be married soon. He looks with favor upon Kabemok," said Wakim's grandmother.

"She is a good girl, and so is her family. They should be very happy. Your family and my family are already related in many ways by many marriages, so we shall all be happy. How soon will they be married?"

"We shall go to Kabemok's family tonight. Perhaps the wedding will be tomorrow. Have your acorns gotten very wormy during this winter?" Once the main subject had been covered, the conversation continued along more casual lines for a polite time. Goodnights were said, and Wakim's grandmother headed towards Kabemok's house. They complied with the ritual entering and were invited by Kabemok's grandmother to join her at the fire. They spoke about various things first before Wakim's grandmother said, "My grandson, Wakim, is a very fine young man, a good man, and he looks with favor on your granddaughter Kabemok."

"He is indeed a fine young man, as my granddaughter Kabemok is a fine girl. She has made many beautiful baskets. She will make a good wife."

"Wakim is young and impatient; he would like to be married soon."

"I think Kabemok would be willing," said her grandmother. "When shall the marriage be? Tomorrow would be a good day— there are no taboos which will interfere. If we wait, there might be a long delay."

It was settled then. There was some further small talk about various matters, and then the two women left, and both families immediately began preparations for the next day.

The grandmother called Kabemok to her. "Everything is arranged for a wedding tomorrow. There are many customs I must now remind you about. One is the custom for a virgin to scratch her husband's face when he beds with her the first time, to show modesty. You must do this to Wakim so that next day everyone will know that you were a virgin. The respect of your husband and his relatives is important to you, and they will judge you by your actions. Your husband must respect you, as you must respect him. He knows he has had you before you were married, and sometimes the man believes you may have been with other men as well. That thought will certainly enter Wakim's mind. Before you are married, a man is often glad if there have been others; he feels safer that way. But after marriage he thinks differently. He might become suspicious of your going into the bush with others. You remember the woman who only gave a man a drink of water and had her nose bitten off by her husband so thta no other man would look at her again. You have started off wrong, so you must be extra careful, not only in that way, but with your husband's relatives. You must exchange presents with them regularly. If you don't, they'll become suspicious, not only of you, but of our whole family. You must be careful about which male relatives you speak to— those with whom you may speak and joke about everything and anything intimate—rutting, defecation, urination, or making love. One of these men, as you know, would become your husband, should Wakim die; they are his brothers, his sisters' sons, his father's sisters' husbands and his mother's brothers, and all the relatives they themselves call brothers.

"Then there are those," continued the grandmother, "with whom you must have nothing to do. You can't speak to them or look at them; you must not even go near them. In fact you must always detour around any place where you even suspect they may be. These are Wakim's father and father's brothers, his sisters' husbands and mother's sisters' husbands, and their brothers. You must learn immediately who these relatives are. To make a mistake of any kind in your husband's family when you are first married will give you a bad reputation. You know all of these men. They are the ones you've avoided since you started getting month-sick. But now there'll be changes in your relationship. You will be Wakim's wife and his relation to them will affect you when you live with them. But you are also related to some of them through your own family; that complication will have to be worked out—it's not unusual at all.

"You must be kind to all of your relatives and so will they be to you. You must hold your temper. They may suspect that you rutted with Wakim, but you must never let on that it is true. Once you are married, not only you but your entire family are married to the husband's family forever, except if enmity develops and poisoning starts—but we must not allow such a thing to happen. Once Wakim is married to you, he can marry your sister, or your brother's daughter, or your father's sister. If you should die after you have had children, we would then give him one of these relatives for a wife so that we can keep the children in our family. So you see, you must do everything to gain their respect and friendship. Now think carefully of all I have said. If there is any more you wish to know, come to me. Now leave me, for there are a great many things to do."

Kabemok walked away, feeling that something had changed her. She was a little frightened and concerned about the future. There was so much to remember and do correctly.

The old grandmother sat near the fire warming herself. "How could I treat that young girl so harshly? She makes some

141

of the finest baskets in the valley. She is so alive and so beautiful, and she's always been a good girl. But I'm an old woman now, and it's hard for me to remember the hot blood of youth, the desire that nothing satiated, not food, not playing games, not work—nothing."

Just the same she found herself remembering the first time she'd been in the bush with that warrior from Shanel. And as she thought she could feel her old blood race through her body. How could she blame the girl for things she herself had done? It was wrong in many ways, but the first man, the man you chose yourself, although he thought he was the chooser, was the one you looked back upon with secret pleasure throughout life.

She had lived a long time, seen many hardships, and troubles, but she'd had much happiness too. Now that she was old she had so many duties they kept her occupied every minute of the day and night, and that was good. For her fires were out, sex was over—and what was an old woman to do if not work? "I am respected and looked up to by all my family," she thought. "Yes, there are many good things in youth and also many good things in old age."

Kabemok was lying in her cubicle, wondering why it was considered so wrong to rut with a man. She hadn't done anything to harm anyone else. She and Wakim loved each other. Why were they upset? Even if she did have a baby, why couldn't she take care of it? Why did these old people always make things difficult, no matter what? Why did they make you feel that you wanted to run away, even when there was no place to run? Why did they think only of themselves? "The family will be shamed. People will talk. It is wrong." And they go on and on and on like that. Why don't they let me alone? It's all right when they do things that I don't like—then it's different. "You're young; you don't know what you're doing. It is dangerous. That boy wants you for only one reason."

She thought of Wakim, a smile playing about her lips, and fell into a sound sleep.

Meanwhile, Wakim himself had come into the sweathouse. He took a place near the old man and announced his news. A flicker crossed the grandfather's face, and Wakim realized that he had started the conversation too abruptly. He praised Kabe-mok and her family. "Our families have been friends for a long time, and I'm old enough, and she's the girl I want." Wakim felt that he was somehow saying too much, but he could think of no other way to put it.

The old man chuckled to himself. It was interesting how every man, even one as dependable and well-trained as Wakim, became self-conscious and uncertain when marriage approached. In a casual voice he said, "I have been waiting for you to get a wife. Yes, you have chosen your bride well, and her family is wealthy and respected. I have noticed lately that you haven't been concentrating too well on your professions—it's time you were married. But there is much you must think of now and be careful about. You will be closely involved with many more people."

It was he who would be advising and teaching Wakim; fathers were occupied in bringing food and money into the family and could not be relied on, for men of that age were frequently away when emergencies arose. It fell to old men like himself who could no longer do arduous tasks to take care of the grandchildren. Now he said, "Although you are already aware of the duties involved in entering a wife's family, I must fulfill my obligation to make it all perfectly clear to you so that no misunderstanding can arise.

"You must aways be careful that you do not speak to your wife's mother, or her mother's sisters or anyone your wife calls 'mother,' for they are all like your wife's mother. If you ever marry another female of your wife's family, it will be one your wife calls 'sister,' whether they be her real sisters or her mother's sisters' children. Neither must you speak to the wives of your wife's brothers. According to our custom, you may marry your wife's brother's daughter, in which case your wife's brother's wife also becomes your mother-in-law. You are not allowed to talk to your wife's father's brothers' wives for the same reason. It is not permissible to touch them or even look at them. If you meet them when you are in the bush, you must detour and turn your back, and they will do the same.

"On the other hand, there are relatives with whom you may joke about the most intimate matters. That is not only permissible, it is done to show friendship. They are your wife's sisters, and those they call sisters, your wife's brothers' daughters, and all the other women whom you may marry, as well as their husbands. However, you must not overdo it; you must have them respect you and be proud of you."

"I know, Grandfather, the joking is very much like I've done with my brothers' wives, my mother's brothers' wives and other such relatives, and with members of Kabemok's family who are already related to me. But tell me about what I must do during the marriage ceremony. Although I have seen marriages before, I haven't paid much attention to the ritual."

The old man told Wakim what to expect the next day. Then he went on, "Of the greatest importance to you in the future will be your wife's month-sick periods. You know something about these matters from living in your own house, and because you are becoming a gambler and a fisherman; so you know how dangerous menstrual blood is. Before a man is married, he does not have to worry too much because he spends so much of his time in the sweathouse, and doesn't touch women—except when he gets a good chance to." The old man's eyes twinkled. "But when you're married, your male relatives are not present to oversee your activities. Your wife will feed you, take care of your clothes and bed, and you will sleep with her. It's important to know about month-sick in advance, or you'll be in great danger.

"You must always maintain your relationships with your own family by giving presents to all your relatives, as you have done up to now. After you are married you will have many new relatives, with all of whom you will exchange presents. You must bring food to them, for their house is where you will eat. You must break yourself of the habit of thinking only of your own family and be careful not to arouse suspicion, for fear of trouble between the two families. If you are careful, you will have two families, and therefore many friends. Your enemies will be afraid to do anything to you because both your families are numerous and rich and have professions. Your families are the only security you have during your life. Now you must tell your father," ended the old man, looking about him.

Wakim too looked around the circle, and saw his father

talking to some men. He walked over and sat beside him and awaited his attention. When his father turned to him, Wakim said, "I have important news—I am going to be married tomorrow to Kabemok."

"So my young Wakim is going to live in another house. Well it's a fine house and family, but isn't Kabemok very young? It seems only a short time ago that her father had to stay home after her birth to take care of her mother."

"No, she is a grown girl, father; she has been wearing her dress with the puberty marks on it for almost a year."

Chapter XIV

MAN of Many Beads opened his eyes to the usual morning activities of a large household. The fire was blazing against the morning chill. A heavy pall of smoke hung shoulder-high, making everyone's head and shoulders almost invisible. There was a good deal of bustle accompanying the arranging of utensils, and the straightening of blankets, as well as a number of children crying. Some of the infants were already greedily sucking at their mothers' breasts.

It was warm now. He stood up, naked like the rest, to join the general movement toward the door. Out of the house they ran, into the raw morning air to the stream, where they jumped in, splashed, and washed themselves. They came out stroking the water from their bodies, laughing and talking.

Outside the house the women, supervised by the old woman, were opening the earth oven. The odor of baked fish and acorn bread made his mouth water with anticipation. Soon Long Haired Woman brought him his breakfast; it tasted as good as it smelled and he ate with great satisfaction. His mother-in-law passed by and spoke to Long Haired Woman about some household matters. Man of Many Beads studiously kept his back turned toward her, according to the custom.

After breakfast he went outside. He still felt slightly self-conscious about the glances cast indirectly at his stubbly eyebrows and wished again that the whole thing had never happened. As he walked he met Long Haired Woman's sister, who said, "Did you have a good time sleeping with your wife last night?"

"Yes," said Man of Many Beads easily, "it is nice to get into bed with a woman. How many men have you been with?" he said in friendly taunt.

She laughed. "Why don't you try to guess?"

He continued on his way, smiling at her teasing.

Meanwhile the women were preparing for the day's work. The old Head Woman was selecting acorns from one of the large storage baskets lining the wall and picking them over in preparation for pounding. Others were straightening up their cubicles, and some were already getting out their materials and the baskets on which they were working. A few had started to mend clothing and prepare skins, and the mothers of young ones were unwrapping their children from their baskets and cleaning them. The children were playing in and about the fires, now and then getting annoyingly in the way, with the women occasionally scolding and chasing them out of doors. But no physical punishment was inflicted because "If you treat a child ugly it will grow up ugly," was the tribal belief.

Man of Many Beads was well-content as he sat with some relatives in the sweathouse. "My power is good—I shall win much money," he said. His old relative seized the moment. "Come, it is time to prepare then." They took their young apprentice with them, a boy who had already learned something of gambling and whom they had given some of their power. They went into the hills where they sweated him, massaged him with angelica root, prayed over him, and sang the proper songs. Then they went to a rattlesnake hole where four beads were thrown four times to the rattlesnake, which came out of its hole and picked one bead up with its mouth. The old man said, "That shows real luck, real power." They walked a bit further, and came to another rattlesnake hole. The young boy was rubbed again, some more songs were sung, then the old man said, "Put your hand inside and caress the rattlesnake." The young boy was afraid, and he paled, but he said nothing. He stretched out on the ground and put his arm into the hole. He felt the snake and caressed it and carefully withdrew his hand. Perspiration beaded his face, but still he said nothing. He would never speak of his fear; his confidence in his relatives was great. More prayers were said, and more songs sung as they danced. Then the three returned to the place where they had prepared their first medicine in preparation for visiting the rattlesnakes. As they walked back they turned their heads to the left four times. When they reached the sweathouse, the young boy was again massaged with angelica root.

Meanwhile a professional fisherman had called his associates and relatives to him and said, "Get ready to go fishing; we'll leave very soon." The oldest living man of his complex, who had been a great fisherman, was too old to do any of the arduous work but still had a tremendous amount of power, much of which he had passed to the younger people. He also retained some of the most important objects, which were repositories for power, as well as some residual expert information. He would pass all this on soon, perhaps for this very expedition, he thought —since he could no longer participate actively. The four younger professionals went home to their bundles of paraphernalia, then went down into the valley where they prayed and sang and danced most of the night, massaging themselves with angelica root the while.

They constructed woven guides, set their large cylindrical fishtraps, put on their costumes, and then took up a solitary vigil, each man placing himself at a different vantage point. One, bearing a two-pronged spear, which was immersed to a depth of four inches in the water, waited patiently in the shadows of a tree, not moving a muscle. Suddenly a large pike came into view. Like a flash the spear moved down and up and the wiggling fish was cast upon the bank. Further downstream two of the men were gradually chasing the fish ahead of them so that they would enter the traps.

That night they slept beside the stream. In the morning, after emptying their traps with dip baskets and nets, they caught some more fish. When the fishing was done they constructed some rough carrying baskets, the only kind that the men ever made, and carried the catch up to the Chief's house.

The Chief, in a loud clear voice that all could hear, called out, "We have much fish here. All you who want fish come to my house." The performance was almost the same as that for the distribution of deer meat. Some of the poorest families who needed food and took some of the large fish left few beads, while some of the wealthy families left more than was their need; it was one way in which the discrepancy in wealth was taken care of.

Chapter XV

THE old men were sitting around the sweathouse talking of various matters. Man of Many Beads felt like entering the discussion but knew that if he did he would be thought forward because of his youth. He looked with admiration at Good Man, at least eighty years old; one of the most respected men in the entire population, he had withstood a lifetime of poisoning, war raids, and all of the other dangers of the world. Good Man had come through life without being punished by the supernaturals. To be like Good Man was most desirable, for when he spoke, though he said little, everyone listened with respect. This was also true of some of the other powerful old men. They were all-important, yet they had a life of ease, for they rarely participated in rigorous activities now, but sat in the sun or the sweathouse enjoying themselves. The young people trod lightly and spoke softly in their presence because they themselves didn't yet have the power or knowledge to live comfortably. It was the old men who made it possible for one to be successful as a hunter. If one were poisoned it was the old people who were wealthy enough to pay for proper treatment by the doctors; they could, on the other hand, also pay very little and leave one to a long lingering, fatal illness. It was the old people who knew and taught the young men the proper prayers and incantations, as well as the skills, and who handed over to you the various objects used to placate the supernaturals. If they did not, you were likely to meet a supernatural, become sick, and die at once. It was the old people who made you powerful for gambling.

The old men made certain that you would comply with their desires; they never gave you all of the information, they never taught you all the skills, and never gave you all the objects, but parceled them out little by little until they were on their deathbeds, thus retaining control as long as they lived.

There were times when Man of Many Beads became discontented, angry and rebellious, but although it had been almost impossible to control himself, he had kept quiet and vented his feelings by walking in the hills. He said and did nothing to antagonize the older men, for he knew the punishments he would face. Still, there were many times he had felt like rebelling. He did the arduous work; he participated in the active gambling and won a great deal of money, yet was given little of the winnings for himself. He was successful in hunting, and yet he seldom got much from the venture. He had wanted a bearcub quiver for a long time and a few good bows that the northern people sold, but he had never managed to acquire enough money to buy them.

He resented all the taboos that made it necessary for him to refrain from contact with his wife for long periods of time because he was preparing for a deer hunt or for gambling or trading expeditions; and he resented taboos which kept him hungry for meat and grease for the same reasons.

Yes, those old men certainly have the best time of all, he thought. Their wives no longer had children, for one thing. For every time his wife had been pregnant he had had to avoid all sorts of activities for nine long months, and even when she was not pregnant, he had to sit around doing nothing during her menstrual periods. "If it isn't one thing, it's another," he thought resentfully. "If you do this, the supernaturals will retaliate; if you do that, human beings will retaliate. You can't travel unless you go at stated times, in an organized large group; otherwise you'll be killed."

He listened to the old men gossiping and talking. After a while, since he couldn't show his displeasure, his irritation, or his rebelliousness, he got up and walked into the brush.

Good Man watched him go with a passive face, although he

was extremely envious. "There goes a young man who has everything," he thought. "He is one of the best deer hunters and one of the most successful gamblers. He comes from a big powerful family, with many professions. He has youth, strength and beauty. I wish I were his age again—when your bones don't ache, you have no worries; you eat meat with your strong teeth and sit and gamble all day and all night without becoming fatigued. That's the age when you can go on a deer hunt, stalk a deer, and act like one, so that you get close enough to kill it with a spear if you wish, while an old man like me stays behind praying and singing for his success. That is the age when we old people give you presents to keep you contented and to make you love us so you will take care of us as we grow older. I have to make sure that I always have enough to last, for one never knows how long one will live. I can't stop giving presents for those who continue to will get food, attention, and respect. If I gave all my valuables and power away, in case of a famine some young reative would kill me without regret, or there would be nothing placed on my cremation pyre. My relatives will have to spend all their money to keep from being shamed in the community, and then they won't have good memories of me. Yes, Man of Many Beads is lucky—he can be with women every night. What pleasure is there left for me? I haven't been with a woman for many years." He sighed, knowing his life to be almost over.

It was an exciting day for all the people of Deep Valley when they received an invitation to Upper Lake. Youngster too had been caught up in the spirit of general preparation for the excursion. "Grandfather," he said excitedly, "I have heard so much about those Upper Lake people, I can't wait to see them."

"I'm glad, my grandson, that you are old enough to make the journey," he replied. "We shall have a Big-Time there; we'll eat some of their very good fish there and bring many more home with us. There'll be trading and gambling, singing, games, and dancing. But best of all I like to think of the lih worms— they are such good eating."

"But Grandfather, if there are so many good times at Upper Lake, why have our tribes been enemies for so long?"

"That dates from a long time ago, when I was a young boy like you. The Upper Lake tribe is about the biggest tribe of people around, and traditional enemies of our people. In those days, their warriors would occasionally come over here and hang around the foothills and when they'd catch a hunter off by himself, or a couple of women and children out gathering seeds or picking berries, they'd kill them just out of revenge and hatred! But our people would do the same to them, it's true.

"One year they caught two of our women and killed them, and our people became very angry because we had made peace with them so that wouldn't happen. That was in the fall, and all winter there was hatred brewing in our people, but nothing could be done after the rains set in. In the spring when the ground had dried, the war chief decided the time had come for revenge. The fish were coming up the creeks; if a party of our men were to pretend to be fishing, the Upper Lake people might be fooled. When the War Chief approached one of the most important Head Men and suggested that we organize a war party to teach those tribesmen a lesson, the old man replied, 'Our people will never be satisfied until something of that sort is done.'

"All the important Head Men were in agreement.

"Then the War Chief went to the Chief, who promised to call a meeting that night.

"At dusk the Head Chief, as was the practice, strolled through the village making his daily evening talk. In a loud clear voice that everyone could hear, he said, 'My people, you must be good to one another, have no hard feeling, use no harsh language, support and uphold one another, be good to your relatives, take care of your children, be good to the unfortunate and old; if any stranger comes around who is hungry, feed him, take him to your home, treat him well.' Then he mentioned all of the Head Men by name and said, 'There will be a meeting of all of these men tonight in the dancehouse.'

"After dinner the Firetender went to the dancehouse and built a fire in the fireplace. When the fire was blazing well, the Chief stood before the dancehouse and called in his loud voice which carried clearly to all ends of the village, 'It is now time for the meeting. The men whose names I announced earlier will now come to the meeting.'

"The men strolled in, single file. It was not customary for men to come in pairs or larger groups. They came in a dignified fashion, slowing their pace if they were too close to the man ahead.

"The Chief then took his seat against the center post on a blanket spread for him by the Firetender. The men filed in and seated themselves, the first man on the Chief's right, the second on his left, and so on alternately, until a large circle was formed.

"When all were seated the Chief announced, 'War Chief wants to discuss a certain matter with you,' and turned the meeting over to the War Chief.

"War Chief said, 'You all know the trouble we have had with the Upper Lake people for as long as we can remember. We have had no peace with them—they have raided our territory and killed our people. We have tried to make peace, but each time they've started all over again. We must now organize a war party because this is the best time to deceive them and get our revenge. Up to now we have punished them individually when we caught them in the hills, but now it's time to have an organized revenge. I will take twelve warriors with me tomorrow morning at daybreak. What do you men think about it?'

"An old man said, 'I think that's the right thing to do. We have suffered at their hands for a long, long time.' All of the other men said approximately the same thing; they were all agreed.

"But the decision to raid the Upper Lake people irked one old man. He had been against such a raid right along, thinking that it would be better to invite the Upper Lake people over for a Big-Time and have some talk. He could foresee a series of retaliatory raids until his people were exhausted and depleted, for the Upper Lake tribe had many more men and resources. But when he had indicated his feeling to the other Head Men, he had found only one other who felt as he did and a few who were undecided; in the end, as was the custom, he and all the rest voted for the war party; to disagree meant having to move away from the tribe to the outskirts of the territory, which in turn meant being always in danger. Any tribe that raided the valley would find and kill your family.

"The Head Chief turned to the War Chief, 'Is there anything more you want to say?'

" 'No,' said the War Chief, 'except that while we are out you must be prepared to hear bad news, but if we have good news to convey to you, we shall come back singing; and when you hear us singing, have the dancers come and meet us. Then we shall all come in dancing.'

" 'That is all,' said the Head Chief, 'we have no other business to attend to. We shall leave the rest to the War Chief.'

"They all left for their homes again, one by one, except the War Chief, who contacted each of the warriors he had chosen to accompany him on the raid, saying, 'I have selected you to accompany me on a raid to the Upper Lake. I want you to be ready before daybreak in front of my house.'

"To the warrior this meant that he would take his spear, bow and arrows, and a small amount of pinole—just enough food for the one day. He would wear his war paint and not encumber himself with any clothing, except for his war bonnet, which was something like a small skull cap with small pointed woodpecker feathers, about three inches high, all around the edge.

"The sky was just getting light in the East. In the West it was still night when the warriors gathered in front of the War Chief's house. When they had all assembled, he said, 'Wey wey. (Now now. We are ready.)' With the War Chief in the lead and the rest following in single file, they started to the East, at a ground-eating half trot. The war leader stopped, he prayed, then threw some beads to the six directions and prayed to the various spirits such as Kuksu, Gilak, Thunder Man, and others. Then the entire group cried out in unison and continued on their way. They reached Scot's Creek in five hours. That's about nine miles from here over those high mountains. They stopped and ate a portion of their pinole mixed with water. After resting for about ten minutes they continued on their way. It is about six miles from there to Upper Lake.

"When they were within a short distance of where the Upper Lake Indians were fishing, they gathered a lot of white willow twigs, leaves, and bark, and wove them into very coarse large carrying baskets which they carried on their backs. They continued toward the Lake. They made certain that some of the Indians in the camp would see them from a distance and think they were ordinary fishermen carrying baskets in preparation for fishing.

"The Upper Lake sentinels who had been stationed as lookouts spied the men carrying the large baskets. One said, 'Those men might be warriors from Shohadjal (meaning Yokiah Valley).'

" 'Oh, no,' said another. 'They are only some of those starving Shohadjal coming over to steal some of our fish. You can see their big carrying baskets.'

"The War Chief had seen the sentinels. He said, 'There are sentinels up there. The people are fishing near the Lake. We'll go behind this hill and throw our baskets away. Then we'll work our way around those sentinels and try to kill them.'

"They examined their bows, loosened the arrows in their quivers, and tested their spears. Then the War Chief said, 'Go slowly and carefully, and get into position. Stay close to me, but not too close.'

"When they had crept to within arrow range, they all saw that there were three sentinels on the hill. They recognized them as famous Upper Lake warriors, with whom they had gambled, danced, and played games during Big-Times.

"The War Chief whispered, "You two take Bitun. You two Mataumatau, and you two take Detaudetau.'

"They moved forward again very slowly and carefully. As they got within close arrow range the sentinels spied them.

"Simultaneously both sides started to shoot arrows. Two of the three sentinels were killed on the spot. The third was wounded. He ran to the Upper Lake fishing camp. As he approached the summer brush houses he dropped in front of the entrance of the first house. With his last breath he said, 'Shohadjal, Shohadjal,' and died.

"The Upper Lake warriors immediately organized a war party and set off in the direction of Yokiah Valley. Our war party had achieved its purpose and was on its way home. They took a more northerly trail for their return trip in order to confuse the Upper Lake warriors, should they follow. They were no longer fresh or energetic. The trail on which the Yokiah warriors had traveled to Upper Lake was the customary trail for both tribes. This northerly trail was less frequently used. They felt elated. There had been a good fight. Both sides had shot many arrows, but they had won, and not even one of our men had been wounded. They moved along at a half-trot with the War Chief in the lead. When they were half-way up the ridge near the Blue Lake, the Upper Lake war party, which had not been confused, approached the foot of the hill. The Upper Lake war leader saw our war party and called to the warriors, 'Who are you? Who is this who did this cowardly, dastardly thing? Name yourselves before I come up and kill you.'

" 'Don't fool yourself down there,' said the Yokiah war chief, 'If you continue to make a fool of yourself, I'll come down there, but I won't shoot you. I'll just club you. Therefore go back and quietly bury your dead.'

"The Upper Lake warriors came no further. They went back from there.

"The Yokiah warriors continued on homeward on the northerly trail. As they came within shouting distance of their village they started to holler, yell and sing, to let the people know that they had been victorious and that the people should come to meet them singing and dancing.

"When the people heard the shouts, yells, and singing, they got their dancing things, put them on, and hurried to meet the War Chief, singing:

> Bitun (He who moves along crouching), You
>   turn your face up toward the sky.
> You turn your face up toward the sky and
>   laugh like I am laughing
> Mataumatau (Foot drummer dancer), You turn
>   your face up toward the sky
> You turn your face up toward the sky and
>   laugh like I am laughing
> Detaudetau (He who hops along like a bull-
>   frog), You turn your face up toward the sky
> You turn your face up toward the sky and
>   laugh like I am laughing.

"From the song in which the War Chief had named the three warriors the people knew that three Upper Lake warriors had been killed and that their own war party was all present. The people all started a real dance on the side of the hill. This was the Kemdem dance, the dance in which they danced while walking along. As they did so, they sang the war song the War Chief had sung. When they stopped, which they did four times, they danced to the ordinary dance song. Finally they all entered the dancehouse, where the dance continued, for four nights.

"The raid broke the spirit of the Upper Lake people. From that time on they made no more raids on our tribe, nor did our people molest them. But hard feelings have continued to exist between us. They never forgot, and neither did we. We have not visited one another since that time. Although we are going over there now, it does not mean that they are not our enemies. We must still be very careful."

"Grandfather, you've told me many times that all the people surrounding our valley are our enemies, but I remember you once told me that the Boonville people helped our people with food."

"Yes, that's true, my grandson. One year the grass seeds in this valley were very scarce, and after our Head Men talked it over they decided that all members of our tribe who had relatives at Boonville would go there with presents to try to get some grass seed. The Chief sent a messenger to the Boonville Chief, who replied that we would be welcome. And a selected group of young strong men and women started off. As we were going through the hills, moving very rapidly because of the danger in the hills, some Yorkville warriors ambushed us and killed one of our men. As our group was small and comprised of women as well as men, we did not try to retaliate. But we returned here and reported the event, whereupon there was much anger, and a war party was organized. The war party then went to Boonville, which as you know lies to the west and south of us beyond the mountains. They are a small tribe but their warriors joined our war party and we then proceeded to attack the Yorkville group. But the Yorkville tribe, expecting a retaliation of some sort, had scouts out who relayed news of our approach and the whole population went into the woods and hills. Our party came upon some old men, women, and children who were slow in retreating and killed them all. We then returned to their village which we burned and completely destroyed. For several years the Yorkville people wandered in the timber; they were afraid to return to their village site. We have been enemies since that time."

"Did we have any other wars?"

"Yes, we have had constant trouble at the northern end of our valley since people are always sneaking in there to hunt and fish and gather food. We have also had war as a result of poisoning. And there have been some wars with tribes over the boundaries. But we are not a warlike people. We do not believe in it, but try to get along with others. We are not like those people over the mountains to the northeast who fight because they enjoy doing so and who take scalps. We've never done that. When we go to war we use the same weapons we use for hunting."

"Grandfather, you said something about trespassing. Wasn't there a lot of trouble about that when my father was a young man?"

"Yes, there was. When your father was young we allowed some people from the north to come into the valley to live. We told them where they could hunt and fish, but as time went on they forgot they were guests and began taking advantage of us. We had trouble with them over a long period of time. At last we attacked, and drove them to Clear Lake where they later had trouble with others, but they have not bothered us since then."

"Once very long ago we had difficulties with the people at Shanel about poisoning. The situation got so bad that the people of both tribes were afraid to come together for a Big-Time. Finally the Shanel chief sent an invitation to our chief to settle the matter by having one hundred warriors of our tribe and one hundred of theirs meet and asked our chief to set the time and place. Our chief agreed and suggested the southern end of the valley. At the proper time both tribes met. The two tribes remained on the slopes of the hills while the warriors lined up in parallel lines approximately 600 feet apart. The two chiefs and their assistants sat on a hill to the east where they could watch all that was going on. At a given signal the warriors on both sides let loose their arrows and used their slingshots. The bravest of the men on both sides moved to positions approximately 100 feet in front of their own groups. The leaders of both sides moved closer to the enemy until they were less than a hundred yards apart. Those in front capered, jumped, and yelled. Our warrior leader said, 'Come on, you old Shanel women, why don't you hit me? I am right here.'

"He was our most expert man. Our warriors knew that when an arrow is white it means it will go over your head; when it is dark you must dodge it.

"As you know, every man paints his arrows differently so that when a deer or some other animal is killed we can always tell who killed the animal. Furthermore, each man puts his own power and poison into his arrows so it will do the right work.

"As this went on, and men began running short of arrows, they told their young sons or brothers to gather up some of the spent arrows that had missed their targets.

"The shouting kept up throughout. You could hear one man say, 'You old cowards—I'm going to kill you. You'd better give up.'

"And many other such remarks were thrown back and forth. Finally we wounded one of their men. When that happened everyone stopped fighting and ran to the wounded man. Then both tribes retired to their own villages. That night our chief made a speech telling our people that we had behaved very well, that now the enmity between the two valleys was over, and that every family should contribute some money as a present to send to the Shanel people. The Shanel chief distributed the sizable gift throughout the valley, giving a large proportion to the family of the wounded man, for they needed it to give him a dance and a feed. Then the Shanel people made up a collection of their own and sent it back to us with an invitation to come to a dance in four days. We did this and had a Big-Time. Since that day we have been more friendly with each other.

"The tribes in the north and east fight differently. There one side tries to drive the other side out of the fight. They pick up the dead bodies, slash them, and remove part of the scalp as trophies. The rest of the body is then handed to the women, who gouge the eyes out and mutilate the corpse. These scalps were kept and danced over in the Victory Dance. When one group chased the other to their village they sometimes burned the village, or they might only say, 'Tell them to stay home and not cause any more trouble.'

"When the victorious party arrived home the war captain would place all the scalps on a stick and the warriors would dance in their war costumes. Sometimes they would shoot arrows into the scalps."

"Grandfather, what was that war about a few years ago in the Lake Country?"

"Oh, that was a bad one, but you must not think there were wars going on all the time—we fight only when we cannot help ourselves. In that case there were nine women and children digging for roots in a little meadow about a mile and a half from the village of Kabenapo. There was a sudden shout and a party of about thirty strange warriors came dashing down the hillside into the meadow.

"When the women saw the warriors coming they called to the children and ran into a little gully. They tried to hide in a live oak thicket where it would be difficult to be overtaken or shot by arrows. Some of the women were killed before they reached cover; the rest were hunted out and killed, with the exception of one woman, Ghalmuk, who was suffered to live because she was related to the invading party. Another woman tried to escape by burrowing into a wood rat's nest. The invaders found her, however, and after torturing her by running sticks and arrows into her vagina, they put her to death."

"Ghalmuk returned to the village before sundown and told the story of the massacre to the enraged and grief-stricken people. A party of about sixty warriors was organized immediately under the leadership of Xadasotiya and went to the scene of the massacre, where they gathered up and solemnly laid out the dead. Then men were sent out to investigate all of the trails. The tracks of the murderers were located and recognized as having been made by Guenoc Indians who live further to the south on the Russian River below and beyond the Shanel. The war party followed the trail all night until they came to a hill from which they could see the Guenoc encamped below. They made their plans and then began gradually working closer toward the main camp, crawling flat on their bellies until they were within seventy-five yards, where they lay motionless until it became light enough to see. Then the war party charged into camp, shooting at everyone in sight. The Guenoc broke in wild confusion and fled into the semi-darkness; seventeen of them lay dead. The survivors gathered in a small group.

"The Lake people went to the top of the hill. Xadasotiya stepped out and addressed the group below. He said, 'This act of ours is a payment. You killed our innocent women and children and this is your reward. I, Xadasotiya, say it.'

"The Lake people then returned to their village. The following day another party was organized, larger than the first. Again wearing their war outfits, and fully armed, they went to the main village of the Guenoc, making no attempt to conceal their approach. When the Guenoc saw them coming, the two parties lined up for battle. Once more Xadasotiya stepped in front of his party and spoke, 'We have repaid you for what you did to our innocent people. We are willing to consider the matter settled. If you wish to fight more we are willing to begin at once.'

"The Guenoc chief stepped in front of his party and said, 'The deed of which you speak was done without the knowledge or consent of our old men. You have taken payment. We do not wish further trouble and are willing to call matters even.'

"The exchange of gifts was arranged, and the matter was settled, but still hard feeling remained, because people don't forget these things.

"Once some Shanel people were out hunting. They saw a group of Indians from the south trespassing on their land. They kept very quiet and followed them. They watched where they camped for the night and saw the women and children settle down. Then they came back to their village and organized a war party. The war leader who was a big, strong and fierce man said, 'I will get those people and beat them to death. I will kill them all.'

"That is how war leaders talk. They got in position that night, and early in the morning rushed on the group and killed all the men, women, and children except two women, whom they tortured and killed in the same way as the Guenoc had done the women of our tribe.

"Another time there was a Chief at Point Arena by the name of Kabekel. The Chief at Stewart's Point was also named Kabekel, and these two were great friends, as Chiefs of villages usually are, but the people of these two tribes were hostile to each other. One time Kabekel of Point Arena, accompanied by his assistants, went down to Stewart's Point to pay his friend a friendly visit. He brought with him many valuable presents, especially beads, sea otter skins, and arrow quivers. The Stewart's Point people took everything away from the visitor and sent him home. He had nothing left.

"When he and his assistants came home ashamed and enraged, the people crowded around their leader. When they heard what had happened, the women wept, and everyone brought him blankets and presents.

"Kabekel addressed them: 'I do not wish to tell you to do anything wicked because I am your Chief. But you would be wise to start making arrows.'

"The Point Arena warriors made arrows for three days. On the fourth day forty-five warriors started out with two brothers from Calim to act as war leaders. These brothers were noted boasters and fighters, who disputed with each other along the way as to who would kill the enemy chief.

"They started off at night, their scouts preceding the war party, and camped outside of the Stewart's Point village. Though it was unusual, Kabekel the Chief went with the war party. At dawn the war party rushed into the village and slaughtered about fifty men, women, and children. The older of the two brothers killed the enemy Kabekel.

"Placing his foot on the head of his dead friend the Chief said, 'My friend, these are the presents that I bring to you, sea otter skins, quivers, and beads.' It was the same speech he had made on his earlier visit.

"As you can see from what I have told you," Grandfather concluded, "wars are of two kinds. There is the formal war between two tribes, which is a means of settling a dispute about a boundary, about poisoning, or some other matter. At such times everything is arranged between the two chiefs with the support of their Head Men and the entire population. This usually occurs between two villages where ill feeling exists between a

164

few families in each of the two groups, and it is a means of stopping trouble. The other kind of warfare is bad because it is in the form of a raid where people are surprised and killed and their bodies are mutilated; such occasions give rise to anger, and mourning, and to continuing ill feeling. Then raids are made in retaliation and eventually lead to more trouble. That is why we don't like raids and only resort to them when we can't help ourselves. Their property, their baskets, their beads, and blankets do not belong to us, and would make us sick, bring bad luck— even the property of those we don't kill would do us harm. The property is burned with the bodies. There are tribes to the northeast who capture women and children, but we never do that because of the danger of poisoning."

Chapter XVI

THE old man had often worried about his hair becoming gray. Several times he and his old wife had gone into the brush where she had examined his hair. Finally she had found a third gray hair. They had not been to the brush for a while, and he thought it was time to try again. He did not want to take any risk of missing the appearance of four gray hairs at one time.

When Old Woman and Old Man found a hidden place, Old Woman took out her tweezers while Old Man undid his hair. Then she carefully parted his hair, and soon found a gray hair. She was praying in a low voice. Old Man sat immobile. Finally she was satisfied; she had found four gray hairs. "Now I can fix you up," she said.

She plucked the hairs out, continuing her chanting prayer, put them in a piece of bark which she had prepared, and said to Old Man, "Spit on this four times and then say, 'Go to My Enemy,' and say his name."

Old Man followed directions.

Old Woman said, "Now you go home."

Old Man felt relieved. It was a disgrace to have gray hair; it was something to be fearful of and would reflect on the entire family. But now he knew that he would have no more gray hair, and that instead his enemy would. It was very difficult to get rid of gray hair. There were only a few people who knew how to manage that, and you could trust only a very close relative with your body.

Old Woman carefully carried the bark containing the hair

and sputum to where the trail forked and the enemy would pass. There she scooped out a hole, meanwhile continuing her chanting prayers. She laid the container in the ground, covered it with the earth, and camouflaged the disturbance. She was torn by conflicting emotions of pride and fear. She was a Power Woman who, by calling upon the Universe about her and all the gods, had concentrated power within herself to such an extent that she could bring retaliation upon the enemies of her family. By her intensity of belief in the supernaturals she was rewarded by their doing what she asked. She had but to ask the supernaturals to kill a person or to make him sick and it would happen. She didn't punish people for trivial matters; she only brought the wrath of the gods down upon serious enemies. But when the concentration of power had become great within her, she had to be extremely careful not to let it affect her relatives, some of whom knew of her power, such as that of transferring gray hair, that she had learned from her older female relatives. But they were not aware that she also had the ability to invoke the gods and bring about her wishes.

Chapter XVII

THE Yomta felt good. It was a warm sunny day. He sat outside his house waiting until the people had all settled down to their daily routine and the visitors had stopped going to the Chief's house. He then stood up and sauntered in that direction. He was content; there was no question but that all of the Head Men of the village and the important participants were in agreement.

When he approached the Chief's house he called out the usual reassuring words and received permission to enter.

He waited to one side of the door until the Chief pointed to a place near him and said, "Rest yourself here."

After the courtesies of eating and chatting had been dealt with, the Yomta said, "I came here to discuss an important matter with you. It has been seven years since we had the ghost dance in this valley. It is time to initiate our young ones. It is our turn this year, and we should make ready for that. The rain has stopped, and conditions are just right."

"What are your plans?" asked the Chief.

"It would be well to have a meeting of the Head Men tonight to discuss this matter," said the Yomta.

"That shall be done," replied the Chief. They spoke about other casual matters again for the prescribed time, and the Yomta departed.

Some of the Head Men had seen the Yomta visit the Chief, and knew that the procedure for the dance had been set in motion. Some of them had already made preliminary preparations.

Man of Many Beads was glad that he and Long Haired Woman had made up and that he had slept with her, for now he would not be able to sleep with her again for many days, or he would invalidate his powers in gambling, deer hunting, and other activities. He was happy, too, that she was not about to become month-sick, which would also, of course, interfere with his activities.

That evening, at dusk, the head Chief, as was the daily practice, strolled through the village, making his regular evening exhortation to virtue in a loud clear voice, which every member of every household could hear plainly. Then he named all the Head Men and called them to an evening meeting in the dancehouse. The Chief had some of the functions of a combination town crier and newspaper, as well as spiritual leader.

After the evening meal, the Firetender, whose hereditary office required a tremendous amount of religious and technical training, went to the dancehouse and started the fire in the fireplace. When the fire was high the Chief stood in front of the dancehouse and called the meeting.

The Head Men who had been waiting for the announcement started to move in the direction of the dancehouse. They came singly, as always, moving into the dancehouse in a dignified manner.

When all of the Head Men were seated, the Chief announced that the Yomta had requested him to call this meeting, and gave the floor to the Yomta.

The Yomta said, "It's time that we made arrangements for the ghost dance and the Kuksu dance. It is time to initiate our young—seven years have passed since we had the dances in our valley, and we must have a feed before we start."

An old Head Man said, "Yes, that will be good. We have had much sickness, and there are many here who need this dance; it will do all of our people much good."

Another old man agreed and added, "There will be much preparation necessary for the devil dance, the pole ceremony, and the others."

Another Head Man said, "Yes, that will be good. Our people are all getting angry with one another. They are getting mean and ugly, and we must do something about the situation, or we'll have trouble."

Another Head Man said, "We must be ready to have a Big-Time as soon as the ground is hard enough for travel. We must make our plans now; we cannot wait until the last day."

Another said, "This should be the right time because food is scarce, and it will be good to have food from the sea and the lake."

As was customary, each Head Man spoke at the council meeting as representative of his entire family. Preparations were always carefully made so that there would be no disagreements. After all had spoken the Head Chief turned to the Yomta and said, "Is there anything more you want to say?"

"No," said the Yomta, "except that it is necessary to have a Big-Time for our mourners before we can really proceed."

The Head Men went out one by one, leaving the Yomta to make arrangements with the Chief.

The next morning the Head Chief added to his usual admonishment the announcement of the planned events.

"All men not in mourning, all who have not lost relatives during the past twelve months, listen to me. Your Head Men have decided to build a new dancehouse for the ghost dance. All not in mourning should contribute money to the collection for mourners so they can have their ceremony before the building begins."

As the Chief gave the definite news, people's expressions changed; at the thought of the excitement and pleasures ahead some childless men and women looked hopeful, anticipating the baby dolls that would be made to help them conceive children, the sex to be determined by the sex of the figurine. Some were glad because their illnesses would be helped by the power of the ceremony. Some looked sad as they thought of their dead, the difficulties involved in the mourning, and that they would not be able to participate fully for that reason. Some women were disappointed because they would be month-sick, or pregnant, and would therefore not be able to participate, and their husbands were disappointed. But in general there was a response of great interest and pleasure.

When the women learned that the ghost or devil ceremony was to be held, they looked forward with fear and trembling to the scourging visit of the dreadful Yukukula (the devil). They all became conscious of the way they had treated their men.

Those who'd had extramarital intercourse became frightened, and even those who had dreamed of it became worried. Some who had made a vow when they had been ill would now be able to fulfill their obligations.

The long tedious winter was now past; the monotony of the daily life and food supply, and the trials which had become burdensome, would all be changed now. The women would sell their baskets, the men would gamble, enjoy the rituals and the dancing. Many thought of their female relatives who had married into other tribes and whom they would now see again; women who had married into the tribe would see their own families who would be visiting. The people talked and laughed outside their houses; they were all animated.

Soon the men began bringing their contributions to the Chief's house. They all waited and looked away while each man put his contribution down on the blanket in front of the Chief. No one watched to see how much each individual contributed; he could give as much or as little as he pleased, depending on individual nature and disposition, wealth or poverty, or his feeling about supernaturals, relatives to be initiated, or his position in the community. All of this, however, was weighed in relation to the entire family, since it was the family, essentially, not the individual, that contributed, and they all desired the good will of the Chief.

After the contributions had been counted, the Chief decided that they were insufficient for the purpose. He tied all the strings of beads together and added some of his own to make up the amount he deemed proper. If there had been more than he calculated necessary he would have kept some for himself. Joining the individual strings assured that the particular amount any individual had contributed would remain unknown.

The Chief then sent his messengers to inform the mourners that they would receive a present in four days. They in turn immediately set about procuring and preparing food for the feast. The men went hunting and fishing, the women began to prepare pinole, acorn bread, and other traditional foods.

Chapter XVIII

ON the appointed day, the Chief waited until the usual morning duties were out of the way. When all was in readiness he said, "It is time for the ceremony. All you people be good to one another. All you people get ready; it is time to begin."

The people who had waited for the announcement gathered together. The Chief led the procession to the house of the mourner that had been designated as the place of assembly. A brush sun shelter had been erected in front of that house, behind which the mourners were assembled, wailing in the traditional manner. Everyone was tense, the wails rose and fell, sending shivers through the hearers. The women scratched their faces and breasts so that the blood streamed. After a short interval of this mourning the Head Chief presented the beads to the chief mourner, who was the spokesman for the others. He in turn passed the string of money to the other male mourners, and they passed it on to the women mourners. As each woman received the string she rose and danced alone, swaying and chanting, with the beads in her outstretched hands, arms extended with elbows pressed to her sides. After each woman had danced and chanted, the beads were placed into a beautifully woven and decorated basket and set aside for sacrifice to the dead.

Then the mourners spread the feast, and the entire population partook of it. After the meal the Head Chief said, "We are going to build a dancehouse, but we wish to do nothing which will sadden you who have so recently lost your relatives. We

173

have therefore made you this offering of money and hope you will not feel too sad."

As soon as he stopped speaking, the mourners began their chant. At the end of it their leader said, "There is nothing wrong with building a dancehouse. We have lost our people, but that is no reason why you should not hold ceremonies and have a good time. They are necessary; they must be held."

All except the mourners took portions of the remaining food with them as they left. Now it was proper to proceed at once with the building of the dancehouse.

The Chief called his messengers to him, gave them directions, told them which villages to visit, with invitations to the Big-Time. The messengers dressed and painted themselves. Each carried a long stave on which were tied some feathers and a bundle of sticks. The sticks were to denote the number of days from the time the messenger arrived at the village that the villagers would be expected to arrive at Yokayo. The messengers started off at a run; and would maintain the pace and stay on well-known rails, holding their symbols of office before them so they would not be considered trespassers and be killed.

Meanwhile the important Head Men selected the site for the new dancehouse; it was centrally located in the village. All the men who were free to do so engaged in its construction. The gamblers immediately started to build up their power for the coming gambling; the dancers saw to their costumes.

Under the supervision of the Yomta, who said the proper prayers, the men worked on the dancehouse. They loosened the earth with digging sticks; then, using platelike and openwork baskets as tools, they threw or carried the dirt to the outer side of the marked-off area. While they dug the sixty-foot hole to a depth of six feet, other men chopped trees for timber, poles, stringers, sideposts, and the other important parts. Notched sticks were used for posts and crosspieces laid in the crotches. After the rafters and stringers had been laid, poles were bound to the stringers with grapevines. Then a layer of woven twigs was placed horizontally on the rafters and another layer placed vertically. This was followed by a layer of grass matting made by the women. Each woman tried to place her grass mat over the particular part of the dancehouse floor where her close male relative would be regularly located. Upon the mats they set a layer of dried grass and then a layer of mud, over which was thrown the loose earth from the hole the men had dug. A smokehole was left in the roof approximately half-way between the apex and the entrance way, immediately over the fireplace.

The tunnel which was the entrance was about fifteen feet long; it was four feet high at its outer extremity and six feet high at the inner opening and five feet wide. A number of emergency openings were placed around the sides of the house that could be kicked open in case of fire or a raid by enemies. The dancing area in the center of the house was spread with a mixture of wet earth, smoothed evenly and covered with a coarse layer of sand.

Everything done in connection with the construction of the dancehouse was done according to exact formula. The center pole was painted with eleven bands, seven red and four white, each about three and a half to four inches wide. Four lines about an inch wide, and alternately red and white, ran spirally around from left to right, and another four from right to left, each set making two complete revolutions of the pole as it went from bottom to top. Each of the sideposts was painted with two white and four red bands similar to those on the center pole. Each of the stringers passing from post to post had three white bands and on the ceiling at a distance of about six feet down from the apex of the roof was a white band about three inches wide, and at about five feet from the lower ends of the rafters a similar band extended entirely around the ceiling. Other bands of red and white paint decorated the dancehouse, and fresh straw was placed around the periphery of the interior.

The drum was a section of an oak log about six feet long and twenty-two inches wide. It was flat on one side and was carefully hollowed out and reduced to uniform thickness of about two and a half inches. This drum was placed on a strong net of grapevines over a pit about eighteen inches deep, with the curved surface up.

In the bustle of activity, the monotony of the winter was forgotten, as were the fights, recriminations, and troubles. The days seemed too short, the nights too long, for all the preparations that were necessary. The young men who were to be initiated were being prepared for their part in the ceremony. The excitement permeated the entire population, even those who could not take part.

Some of the men were prepared to trade money and baskets for good bows made by the people to the north. The Lake Country people were expected to bring food for sale.

All the men who were to participate had been careful to observe the taboos connected with the coming dance. They had sweated, rubbed themselvs with angelica root, and fasted. There would be no meat or grease for them until after the dance. The number of days of fasting varied according to their level of office. They were circumspect in their behavior, for a mistake would be dangerous not only to the individual and his family, but to the entire community. This was the most religious and important Big-Time of the year.

The gamblers were going through the same preparation. They were careful not to indulge in sexual activity. Even to dream of sex was dangerous. The shadow of a menstruating woman would invalidate the power. These were the nights they spent in the sweathouse. As for the women, they were glad that the men were not underfoot. They were busy cleaning up their houses, taking stock of their baskets, money, food, clothing, and implements, and preparing food, not only for the feasts, but also so that they would be as free as possible during the dance period.

Meanwhile the invited tribes were also in a state of excitement. They too had had a long hard winter, full of troubles and difficulties. They had prepared various articles for sale and trade. The Chief had discarded a stick from the messenger's bundle each day. On the morning that he threw the last stick away, they would start on the journey. It was very early in the morning of the starting day that he strolled through the village, addressing the people in his loud official voice.

"We are ready to leave for Deep Valley tomorrow," he said. "You must behave properly, for you are visitors. Do not win all our hosts' money when you gamble nor lose all your money. Be friendly with those people, be generous, and don't make trouble. Those of you who must stay behind because you are too old, or for other reasons, take care of things while we are gone. We are ready to leave now."

It was still dark, and they would start as the first indication of light appeared in the eastern sky. Some of the men who were to participate in the coming ceremonies were still in the hills, preparing themselves. The village would be quiet and seem empty when those who would take part had left. Some of the young boys and girls stood around trying to conceal their disappointment; their playmates would be initiated and they wouldn't; they would have to wait until next year or maybe a few years until everything again coincided properly. There was disappointment throughout the group that was to be left behind, for this was a powerful Big-Time that would bring good luck. There was a sense of strain and disgruntlement in the attitudes of all the home-bound members as they went about taking care of the daily tasks.

The men and women gathered around the waiting Chief were carrying their babies in baby baskets, other things in big carrying baskets with tump lines around their heads. They started off, keeping close together. The War Chief had designated his scouts, who flanked the column and preceded it, as a protection against enemies. That night they reached a pleasant spot close to the Yokiah village and camped there.

"When these people come here you must treat them right," said the Yokiah Chief in his official talk on the eve of the Big Time. "They are invited visitors, so do not grumble nor get angry, but watch your actions. They have come a long way and will be tired. Do not be stingy. Respect their old people. We don't want to make enemies; this is the time for peace and good feeling. It is important for everyone to do as he is supposed to do. Then we shall have friends all over."

By this time he was in front of the new dancehouse. He approved of the preparations made for their guests. "It is good. You have brought much wood for the visitors. You have fixed up a nice dancehouse, you have placed clean straw inside on which they will be able to sleep, and there is sufficient wood for cooking their meals."

On the hills fires appeared here and there, each one representing the encampment of a visiting group. As was the custom, each visiting group would spend the night close to the village the night before the dance was to begin, lighting a bonfire to make their presence known, and making final preparations for their arrival in the morning.

Chapter XIX

IN the early dawn light, Man of Many Beads watched the strangers coming into the village. They looked exactly like his own people. The naked bodies of the men were a warm dark red-brown color. They were a brawny group; mature males looked as if they weighed about a hundred and eighty pounds, and were about five feet ten inches tall, although some were inches taller and many pounds heavier. The mature women were more squat and ran to fat, but the young women were slim and beautiful. The features of both men and women were uniform and regular; their lips were well-formed, and their teeth strong, even, and white. There were no jutting chins, beetling eyebrows, or hooked noses; in general, they were very handsome. Some of them wore wrap-around moccasins, but most went barefoot. They all wore strings of money around their necks and waists; the white clamshell money was beautiful against their dark bodies. The men wore nose and ear plugs, decorated with beads and feathers. Their long straight black hair, well-combed and set with bone hairpins, had been decorated with varicolored feathers. Faces, bodies, and arms were tattooed in simple line decorations.

Some of the women wore the usual dress of buckskin and skirt with the hair on the inside and the skirt overlapping and tied into position. Some had wild cat skins over their shoulders; others sea otters', the most prized possession. A few well-tanned panther hides were also in evidence. Some wore coats of shredded tule. Outer garments which hung from the shoulders covered the breasts of some women, but others wore nothing from the waist up. The costume varied with the individual taste, but the borders of most of the women's skirts were decorated with yellow hammer feathers, and beads and shaped pieces of abalone shell dangled from the hems. Here and there in the group there were girls who had attained puberty but were not as yet married. These had four rows of red paint on their skirts. As soon as a girl married, the red paint was removed.

Many of the women wore wristlets an inch and a half to two inches wide made of the finest, most delicate beads. The married women could be recognized at a glance by wedding belts they had received from their families via their husbands on their marriage day, belts seven or eight inches wide, varying in length from ones just encircling the waist to others twice as long. The women wore decorated and etched earplugs. The younger girls were tattooed on their legs and arms; the older women on their faces as well. The finery varied according to wealth. Some had very little, while others wore elaborate necklaces with a variety of pendants which reached almost to the ground. A neckband of fine feathers, about an inch and a quarter wide, was worn around the neck, and tied together at the back. In the front, about a half an inch apart, long strings of money reached almost to the ground. Some had pieces of Indian gold, some pieces of varicolored abalone shell, some had "big" money, and some dried and cured woodpecker scalps attached to the ends, and combinations of all these were also intermingled with quail plumes and red and green feathers.

The men too wore money. The married ones also had feather belts which they had received from their bride's family at the time of marriage.

The young women were beautiful and moved with a lithe grace. With their regular features, well-formed bodies and high, pointed breasts, they made an attractive sight. The moderate-sized features so becoming to the young girls seemed too small for the obese older women, many of whom weighed well over two hundred pounds and some close to three hundred and fifty.

Man of Many Beads wondered how such beautiful young girls, who made your skin tingle and your blood race, could become so fat, and then later on become like some of the old women in his village, who weighed little more than ninety pounds, whose breasts hung slack as burst bladders, whose skin was shriveled and whose bloodshot eyes protruded because of all the smoke they had endured throughout the years.

The visitors made a wonderful sight. All their decorations revealed a great delicacy of workmanship and were in excellent taste. They wore no garish, clashing colors, and bore themselves with an air of dignity, pride, and self-respect. There was no arrogance, no aggressiveness, no exhibitionism apparent, only a calmness, an assurance, an entire lack of any connotation of servility, ingratiation, or fawning. They were a proud people, an alert people, yet Man of Many Beads knew how they could abandon themselves to enjoyment at the proper time.

The Chief led the procession with a group of the important men immediately behind him. He was weighed down by the burden of a long string of money, which had been collected from his entire group.

Man of Many Beads wondered at the assurance of the visitors. He knew that when he had gone to other valleys on trips of this kind he had felt elation and anticipation, but he had also been conscious of the fact that one might always expect enemies. He knew that some feuds had gone on for many generations and that the dangers of being poisoned during one of these Big-Times was great. Yet he could also understand their attitude, for although all of the dangers were known and anticipated, and although many of those strangers had themselves prepared poison for this occasion, and had even coached their sons and daughters to have sexual intercourse with certain individuals in order to poison them, these trips were always enjoyable nevertheless. He had always wanted to be able to visit certain places, and had been on the verge of doing it more than once with his *awihinawa*, but to do so would have meant only one thing, that they were trespassers and might well be killed.

By this time the procession had approached the dancehouse. The lookout stationed on the roof of the dancehouse had called to the Head Chief who was inside, "They are here."

The Head Chief came out immediately and took his position directly in front of the dancehouse. He delivered a short oration, saying, "We are very happy and pleased that you good people have come to help us in having a Big-Time. We want you all to enjoy yourselves. There is wood here for your fires. We have provided places inside for you to sleep. We want you to enjoy yourselves while you are with us."

The visiting Chief replied, "It is fine to be here. All of my people are happy that you good people have asked us to come."

The Head Chief said, "We would like you to come into the dancehouse; you are very welcome to us."

As the visitors entered, each group was assigned to its particular position in the dancehouse. They seated themselves, with their Head Chief, heads of families, firetenders, and other officials ranged in front of them.

As group after group approached the entrance where the Chief was waiting, he recognized them and welcomed each in their own language, for the Chief was a man who knew the languages of every tribe in the whole area. It gratified him to see that all the invited groups had come.

Some distant tribes, not able to come as a group, had only been able to send a few members, but for all practical purposes all the groups in the entire area were represented. At the last ghost dance, in the Lake Region, there had been fewer people present since that was in the eastern extremity of the area.

It was the religious ties that gave the Pomo Universe a kind of totality. When the tribes came together all group enmities were submerged, although the personal enmities of individuals and families might remain keen. Although poisoning was frowned upon by the Chiefs and Head Men, some individuals nevertheless—secretly, as always—carried out their plans.

The ceremonies were directed at unifying the group made up of these diverse populations. The occasion was a means of easing hatreds and difficulties, which everyone was aware existed among the various tribal groups as well as among and between families and individuals; nevertheless, there was at least a superficial putting aside of these conflicts during the entire period. All participants did their utmost to maintain a facade that would arouse no suspicions. They all knew that as soon as the ceremony was over and they departed the truce would be ended. It was even to be expected that raids might take place immediately, and that if anyone became sick soon afterward it would undoubtedly be because that person had been poisoned during the Big-Time. Retaliatory measures would then be immediately initiated, and trouble would ensue. For the rest of the year the territory would be again composed of individual tribes, each of them composed of individual families, and each of them composed of a number of intermarried individuals. Only occasional trading parties would bring two tribes together.

After all the visitors had taken their places the Head Chief entered the dancehouse. The oldest visiting Head Chief invited him to the other Head Chiefs' sitting. Then each of the visiting Chiefs made a short speech, each speaking ritualistic phrases: "Our people are very glad to be here with you. It was very nice of you to invite us to this Big-Time. We have brought with us a little present from our people to your people."

Each then handed the long, generous string of money to the Head Chief. When all this ceremony was done, the Head Chief and his assistants took the money to his house. That money later would be divided among his own people on the basis of the wealth of each family, the amount of food they had contributed to the big feed, the part that members of a particular family had taken in the Big-Time, and various services rendered during the entire ceremony, the money being given directly to each family's Head Man.

After the formal reception the visitors made themselves comfortable; the dancehouse area was packed with men, women, and children visiting both inside and outside the dancehouse. A spirit of gaiety and expectation had permeated the gathering.

It was during a Big-Time of this kind that the entire Pomo universe could be understood in its broad sweep, as well as its particulars. The intertribal and international relations became manifest. The interpersonal relations of the individual as an individual, as a member of a family, as a member of a profession, the limitations of sex, age, and other aspects, came more clearly into focus.

There was a happy feeling of expectancy in the crowd as people continued to come in. The costumes shone and glittered in the light.

Each small family unit talked and laughed in a subdued

183

fashion. The younger children were quiet and placid but looked about them continually in their great curiosity and shyness. As the building filled they got over their feelings of strangeness and soon started to run about, yelling and laughing and stumbling over the adults without inviting reproach.

The firelight cast a warm glow over the assemblage. The dark warm skins, the red and green feathers, decorated dresses, long white strings of money, the sparkle of the multicolored abalone shell jewelry, the constant movement, all made a scene of beauty and color.

The cultural controls and self-disciplines which kept individuals in check became relaxed during these dances. Husbands and wives, clandestine lovers, married and unmarried, and newly-met boys and girls had sexual intercourse in the brush. Such encounters were never public; always private and secret. The fear of poisoning, the aggressions held in control, the expansiveness of large crowds, and the submergence of the individual during the almost hypnotic dances, all helped bring about this state of affairs.

The rhythmic movements of the dance, the swaying of bodies, the holding still of the torsos while the legs moved in unison, the varicolored, delicate headdresses moving and vibrating, all tended to bring the audience to a semi-hypnotic state.

Chapter XX

THE excitement of the past two weeks, the physical exertion, lack of sleep, the intensity, the concentration on learning his part in the ceremonies, had all taken their toll of Step-Along. Now it was evening again and he was tired. He sat with his people on the side of the dancehouse, half-drowsing, while the people milled about, talking, visiting, and settling themselves for the evening ceremony. The fire was burning brightly. There was a contagious animation in the crowd, but he was immune to it. Men and women were calling to one another in good-natured banter. An old man called out, "Where are the dancers?" Someone else replied, "Why don't you put the feathers on, Old Man?" Drum Man took his position at the drum, stepped on it, stamped it lightly once or twice. Suddenly there was a cry; the head singer took up his position with his split rattle in his right hand, raised it above his head, rattled it a few times, called out again, and started the song. The men grouped around him, and, with cocoon rattles and split rattles, kept time with him. When he came to the chorus of the song, they joined their voices to his. Then the dancers appeared. The women had been taking their places; they formed a half-circle and swayed in unison. There was little other movement; they remained in one spot. One of the dancers appeared from behind the brush screen, simulating a bird, because these were their ancestors, the bird people. This was a happy dance, a dance of pleasure. As the drumming and singing continued and all the dancers appeared, Step-Along felt his whole body respond to the beat. There was a short rest period after a pause in the dancing, after which it began again.

All of his tiredness had disappeared. He was sorry now that he hadn't worn feathers and danced. Every member of the assemblage felt the contagion of the rhythm; the group moved as one. As he watched the women swaying there gradually came over him the feeling of sexual motion. Their breasts—firm, rounded, pointed, seemed to become more enticing. The white beads swayed and rubbed between the breasts against the dark skin, the firelight warming its tones. The men dancing were virile and strong. They advanced upon the women, and the women turned their bodies slightly to one side, then to the other, enticing the men.

The main dance was beginning. The women had formed ranks; the singers sang to the symphony of the flutes, whistles, and rattles; beating time in unison with the foot drum, the first dancer appeared from behind the screen. He stamped the ground, looking about him, keeping time with the music, his feet dancing out an intricate rhythm. Suddenly he moved forward and took his place on the dance floor, where he continued the rhythmic motions. The second dancer appeared from behind the screen, repeated the actions of the first, and then the others appeared one by one. All kept perfect time as they pounded the ground with an intricate toe-heel sequence, raising their knees high, keeping their trunks in one position. At the proper signals they displayed their abilities and virtuosity by making first one part of their headdress move and then another, making the feathered sticks vibrate, all the while beating their rhythm on the ground until the earth reverberated and every pulsebeat of that multitude increased in tempo and maintained the cadence of the dance. Suddenly, at a cry, the dance was over. A great relaxation took the group. Then the music began again. And again the multitude, but now in a shorter period of time, was in harmony, their intensity even greater. A third and a fourth dance followed. By the end of the fourth dance the people, the dancehouse, the earth, the entire universe pulsated. The tension was so great that when the dance suddenly ended, the traditional "ho" came out in unison and the relaxation, or rather the reaction, was like a sudden cry on a still black night.

Again there was a short period of rest and then the third period of the traditional four times four dance sequence was started. The dance continued.

Step-Along looked at Young Woman. She was beautifully formed. He had noticed her many times during the past few days and had tried to speak to her. But each time there had been people about, and she had acted shy and not replied. But now as he watched her he felt that she was dancing for him alone. Every muscle of her body, every seductive twist and turn seemed to be directed at him and was being made for him alone. When the dance suddenly ended, Step-Along could not contain himself. He stood up and left the dancehouse to go into the brush. He was in a fever of passion, and the cool air felt good against his naked body.

The dance started again. The thumping rhythm of the foot drum entered his body, he felt the very ground vibrating.

Young Woman had watched Step-Along's eyes upon her, watched his face become tense, his eyes devour her. As she swayed enticingly she felt that she was swaying for him. She noticed him leave the building, and, taking off her headdress, she went outdoors also. Many people were standing around outside talking and laughing. She stopped a moment and spoke to a few of them and gradually moved away and started walking into the brush.

Such close proximity of human beings for the last few days had had its exciting effect. Young Woman felt herself glow with an internal warmth that was intense, new, and afforded her ecstatic pleasure. As she walked into the hills she felt the vibration of the drum; it permeated her entirely. Her every nerve was in tune with it, her body tingled.

Step-Along started to walk back to the dancehouse, his body shivering from the throb of the music. His entire being was filled with excitement. When he was still some distance from the dancehouse he saw Young Woman detach herself from a group near the entrance, and start walking into the brush. She could not see him but she was coming in his direction. He moved to where he could intercept her, waited until he could reach out and touch her, and whispered, "Don't be afraid, this is Step-Along." Young Woman remained silent, unable to move. Step-Along put his hands upon her breasts, and felt the nipples harden.

Their bodies joined to the rhythm of the drum.

Chapter XXI

IT was time for the devil dance. The dancehouse had been cleared, and the doorkeeper allowed no one to enter who was not a member of the society pledged to secrecy.

The speaker climbed to the top of the dancehouse. He announced to the women, children, and uninitiated men gathered in a large group some distance before the dancehouse, "We are going to be visited now by the people from the world below. They are coming here because you women have not been good to your husbands, because you have rutted with other men, and because you have had thoughts you should not have had. You have done many wrong things that you should not have done."

The Head Chief had sent a messenger to notify the dancers who were stationed all about in the hills. They had built small fires at designated spots to give notice of the fact that they were ready. The crier was at his position on the roof of the dancehouse just below the smokehole. He gave the ghost call, "Ye, ye, ye, ye."

At once, answering calls came from the ghost dancers scattered all over the hill, singly and in pairs. The ghost response was given by them, "Wau wai, wau wai, wau wai, wau wai."

The crier continued his calling until some of the dancers appeared on the outskirts of the village.

The devils came in from the hills, capering, dancing, jumping; flames burst from their heads and back in great volume; they were yelling and calling. Their bodies were painted in fantastic colors, some held live rattlesnakes in their hands. They came dashing at the assemblage.

The terrified women and children started milling and running, but the men who were with them huddled them into a circle. They swung blazing firebrands in the air, yelled, and made frantic dashes at the marauding and blood-thirsty devils to fight them off from the women and children. It was a spectacle which struck fear into the hearts of the assembled hundreds of women who were screaming and fainting and clinging to their valorous protectors. Finally all the devils penetrated the dancehouse.

The bravest of the men entered and held a parley with them. While this was going on there suddenly came rushing upon the women and children another devil wearing a feather mantle on his back, reaching from the armpits down to the mid-thighs. He was zebra-painted on his breast and legs with black stripes. A large headdress topped this costume. His arms were stretched out at full length along a staff passing behind his neck and across his shoulders. He dashed at the women, capering, dancing, yelling, and calling. The women and children ran for their lives, surging back and forth to keep distance between themselves and the devil. If a woman was so unfortunate as to touch any part of the devil or his costume, all of her children would

After they had all disappeared, everyone was herded into the into the mountains.

with a tremendous row and racket of sham-fighting were chased die immediately.

At last the devils were expelled from the dancehouse and dancehouse. The Head Chief took his position before the entire assemblage, held a rattlesnake before him. Slowly and sonorously he began speaking, "Women do as they please. That is wrong. Women must be good to their men. They must do what their husbands and older male relatives tell them to do. They must do what is right and proper. Otherwise these devils will bring harm to our whole people." Brandishing the rattlesnake in his hand he said, "We must beware; the dire wrath of Yukukula will be your just desert if you do not live lives of chastity, industry and obedience." The women reacted with terror to this speech; they shrieked aloud and fell swooning on the ground.

Back in the hills the devil dancers were removing their costumes. Their leader was content. Although the affair had

190

appeared to be a mob scene without rhyme or reason, each man had been carefully trained in his proper part, the route he was to take, the timing, and every other detail. The pitch that had been used to cause the flames on their heads and backs had lasted throughout the ceremony. All the costumes were carefully put away with the proper ceremony and prayers, and all the paraphernalia put under the superivsion of the chief Kuksu doctor. It was he who safeguarded it during the long intervals between ceremonies.

Meanwhile the ghost dancers were getting ready. Each, in a secluded place in the brush, rubbed his body with chewed angelica root while reciting the prayer for long life, good health, and prosperity for himself, his fellow dancers, the people of his village, and all the guests. Asking the supernaturals to lend him a striped skin, he painted his body in stripes, using white, red, and black paints; or he covered it entirely with one of these colors, or the upper half with one color, the lower half with another. One could also paint the right and left sides differently, or select a design of bands and stripes. All wore a headnet filled with down, with feather tufts on top of the head and a yellow-hammer quill forehead band fastened across the forehead. A short girdle of pepperwood branches about the waist completed the costume. At a prearranged signal they all came in from the hills, each carrying two bunches of grass or twigs, and on approaching the dancehouse stood for a moment with outstretched arms. At this moment the crier shouted, "O, o, o, carry health to the village, carry health to the girls, carry health to the chief, carry health to the chieftainesses, carry health to the children."

The people in the dancehouse shouted while the drummer beat rapidly. The head singers took up their cocoon rattles and went outside, singing, to meet the dancers and escort them into the dancehouse. The dancers ran in shouting. Each new dancer went through exactly the same motions and cries.

These dancers performed various comic antics, such as pretending to be stung by wasps and doctoring one another. Each ghost dancer entered the house backwards and started toward the drum. He made believe he had made a mistake, and stopped. Finally he inquired his way, inverting his words, and the spectators replied with inverted statements also. "You must go on the west side," meant that the dancer was to go down the east side of the dancehouse.

Contrary to the usual procedure, a special place was marked off for the dance. The regular dancing area was in front of the center pole, and the ghost dance itself was actually performed by marking off another area, and various other signs gave evidence that the spirits must always do things differently from mortals. Their dress and conduct, their reversal of terms of direction, their grouping, exemplified the conduct of the spirits of the departed, who find everything strange when they return to the realm of mortals. When the chief ghost dancer arrived in front of the center pole he said, "Mamule." The spectators replied, "Hehe." Then he made a short speech in an archaic language, which meant, "I do not come to do anyone harm, but rather to take all sickness away and make everybody strong."

The entire dance was one of strict ritual and ceremony. In conjunction with the ghost dancers were the ash devils or fire eaters. These were entirely nude except for a coat of blue paint and the black, red, or white paint on their faces, which were also disguised by masks of green twigs. Some of the paint had been scratched off their legs with fingernails to show the skin.

The fire eaters were privileged to perform many comic antics. One or more of them ran up the roof of the dancehouse from the outside and dove through the smokehole, which was about eighteen feet off the ground. (The uninitiated, on the outside, did not know that a special net had been stretched about two feet below the smokehole to catch the dancers). During this exhibition a post was set in the ground beside the net so the dancer could slide down. After this he took up a position at one of the posts near the door to levy tributes of firewood, tobacco, or other commodities on the spectators.

When the chief ghost dancer arrived at the drum he said to the assembled group, "We have come from the hollow stems of the grass, crawling like snakes, to visit you. We have come for your good. We have no evil motives, we have come to bring you good health and happiness, not sickness and misfortune. We will make you all healthy, we will bring you all good luck."

Then he went through a ritual intended to accomplish all these things.

The ghost dancers performed their ceremony four times during the day: at dawn, late morning, early afternoon and late afternoon, after which there was a ceremonial disrobing, and then a swim and bath in the river.

The ash ghosts were in and about the dancehouse, wearing headnets, feather hats, and grotesque makeup of clay on their faces. Each carried a stick a few feet long, with a carved cranehead fitted with abalone eyes, a feather hat, and other ornamentation.

The fire was only a bed of coals, providing barely enough light to allow anyone to grope his way about. After everyone had gathered, a moaning started as if it were coming from beneath the ground. The moaning grew louder, then a powerful voice yelled, "Wa-u-wao."

The Yomta called for light, the fire blazed and illuminated the assembled ghosts, the Yomta standing as master of ceremonies beside the drum, surrounded by the ash ghosts with their craneheaded staffs. It was an awe-inspiring sight. All the men were prostrate before them, and the youths about to be initiated trembled with fear.

During the ceremony the ash ghosts did everything they could to draw a laugh from the spectators. There was a familiarity in their speech and activities that did not exist in the everyday life of the people. The purpose of this was to establish a relationship between the living and dead and give the initiates a sense of power and control that would help them understand the after world, which had so many counterparts in everyday life, and all the activities of the living. An ash ghost said, "The Yomta is an ugly man; someone told me that."

The Yomta replied, "You are only a joker; you meant my dead grandfather."

There were running comments between the ash ghosts and the men on the floor, all involving saying things backwards and expressing the contrary of what was meant. The boys who were to be initiated were called little squirrels. The ash ghosts tried to make the people laugh. If a spectator were unable to control

193

his laughter the ash ghosts made an exaggerated complaint to the Yomta, demanding a forfeit of strings of bead, "eight times that long" stretching arms to their full extent.

The old man had to pay. The pay consisted of two or three beads strung at wide intervals on tule.

One old man was very rude in his reply and his laughter and wanted to leave during the ceremony.

The chief ash ghost began his ritual. He held up his crane-headed staff as though it were a bow and he were hunting for squirrels. He danced over to the drum, tramped on it, then went out among the spectators, performing all kinds of antics. He found no squirrels, and returned to the drum, complaining about his failure during his long hunt. Then he hunted for a singer (humming-bird). The ash ghosts were dancing and circling about, holding the crane-heads before them. Each went to the fire, picked up a hot coal, moved it from hand to hand, carefully examining it, tossed the coal in the air, caught it in his mouth, danced and ran about the assemblage, blew upon the coal until it flared up and sparks flew out, and finally leapt upon the drum and beat a rapid tattoo on it.

One of the ash ghosts became "irritated." He jumped into the fire, throwing hot coals among the assemblage, but the chief and firetenders put their official sticks across the fire, and he had to stop.

The ash ghost was on a squirrel hunt again. He spied one of the initiates, made a dash for him, grabbed him and tossed him across the fire to the others, who continued the tossing back and forth for a few moments, until the head ash ghost said, "This boy will take the place of his older relative in four or five years."

Some of the ghost dancers were offended because the supply of wood had run down. They ran to the fire and started throwing it all about the dancehouse. The two fire-tenders ran over to the fire and held two sticks over it, which made the fire taboo to the ghost dancers. Some of the ash devils immediately came over with their special bird-shaped staffs, which gave them absolute control of the entire assemblage, including even the Head Chief. These supernaturals were in control. The fire-tenders, who were officers of the dancehouse and mere mortals,

194

had to remove their restriction. And the ghost dancers were then privileged to do as they wished since they were under the patronage of the ash devils.

The ash devils served as messengers, sergeants-at-arms, and collectors of fines during the regular ghost dance. They were the special clowns who performed all manner of antics, in their endeavors to make the spectators laugh. Whenever someone laughed or even smiled, one of the ash devils would run at him with his wand and levy tribute. In one case it might be a payment of beads, in another a penalty of an activity, such as requiring the offender to bring wood or to sprinkle the dance floor with water between dances. Some of the dancers would see spectators in possession of something desirable, and send the ash devils to him to demand the desired article. Then the owner would bring it forward to the foot of the center pole and deposit it.

Some of the ash devils propped their eyelids open with small wooden pegs, giving them a fierce and comical expression. Some stretched their mouths out of shape, or filled their cheeks with dried grass, which they blew out in a cloud.

Renowned singers were called upon from time to time to rise and sing.

After the ash devils started their ceremony, no one was permitted to speak a word during the entire time. They arranged themselves in position around the center pole, then suddenly jumped into the fire and began throwing hot coals among the spectators. Someone started to sing a song, at which the ash ghosts stopped throwing the fire about. Then the dancing started. All was very quiet. A large fire of manzanita wood had died down to a bed of hot coals, the hottest of which had been put to one side. (Manzanita wood was used because it burned hotter and made firmer coals.) One of the fire dancers went over to the hot bed of coals, put his hand into it, pretended to be burned, and danced about as if he were in great pain. He danced to the center pole and struck it with his hand; at once the pain vanished and the burn disappeared. The pole was ice, and cooled his hand. Then the fire-eaters went through a religious ceremonial dance; each one danced to the fire, put his hands into the bed of coals, carefully selected a coal that suited him, slowly shifted it from his left to his right hand, and then continued to dance. He threw it in the air, caught it in his mouth. He danced slowly while he faced the spectators, breathing upon the coal, until it glowed and sparks blew. Then he danced to the drum where he beat a rapid tattoo. This continued for quite a while.

It was time for the Yomta to illustrate their supernatural powers of bringing dead people back to life. The ceremony started with a lively dance, in which all the men and women participated. There was general singing, accompanied by the sounds of the various instruments—the whistle, the rattle, the split-stick and the foot drum. The chant was lively. The women lined up, forming a background for the men, who moved about in their dance. In addition to their costumes, the women wore headdresses with large puffs of yellow-hammer feathers hanging from sticks protruding a few inches before their eyes. The men had mantles of buzzard, hawk, and eagle feathers reaching from their armpits down to their thighs, and circular headdresses of the same material. The women formed a large semi-circle and the men danced within it. The women swayed their bodies, each holding a string of beads in her outstretched hands. The swaying of the women became a very subdued and controlled expression of feminine sexuality; the men in their turn portrayed a masculine virility. When the dance came to an end, the male performer, provided with a spear and accompanied by his prompter, took his place in the ring. A nude woman squatted on the ground in the center. The head singer started his chant, and the prompter signaled to the performer to begin. He danced and then made a furious sally, with his spear stabbing the empty air. Then he turned and dashed in the opposite direction and stabbed into the air again. After doing this a few times he stabbed at a woman in the audience. All the while the prompter kept chasing him backward and forward, until, at a cry from the prompter, the performer ran at the woman and stabbed her through the stomach. She fell over on the ground, quivering in every limb. The blood ran forth in a flood. The Indians all ran to her, and carried her to one side, where she was laid out for the funeral pyre, after which the doctors doctored her and she became well again.

The men, with all proper ritual and prayer, had prepared a pole 35 feet long, a tree trunk trimmed of its branches and peeled. A hole, large enough to receive the pole, had been dug directly in front of and a short distance away from the dance-house, into which the pole was now to be set. The men who were to participate in this ceremony had gone into the hills and dressed in their special attire and painted their faces and bodies. At the head dancer's word, chanting and dancing, they brought the pole into the village and laid it down in front of the dance-house. A streamer had been attached to one end of it, which the fastest runner in the village held in his hand. The other men, arranged in the order of their speed, lined up along the pole. Behind them was a line of women. Ceremonially, the pole was picked up and the men began a wheel-like movement, with the butt of the pole held directly over the hole. As they ran faster and faster the pole swayed up and down, and the women followed, throwing handfuls of small parched blackseed on the men. When four circuits had been made, the headman shouted, "Ha . . . u . . . ," and the pole was immediately lifted into place, the call being repeated as this was being done. Stones and earth were placed in the hole around the butt of the pole and tramped into place.

The Kuksu dancers came out of the hills and stopped 200 yards away. The men began climbing the pole while the women threw balls of uncooked meal made of grass seed at them. The climbing ceased. The children who were to be initiated, ranging in age from five to ten years, were herded about the base of the pole. The Kuksu dancers danced to the pole, took the children in hand, made them lie down upon the ground and covered them with blankets. The head Kuksu dancers supervised the ceremony, which was performed by an old man who had been selected not only because of his long life and good health but particularly because of his good-heartedness. The object of the ceremony was to secure good health for the children and make them grow rapidly. This was one of the most important phases of the initiation, and the entire life of a child depended upon it.

The children were told not to look up under any circumstances. Then the old man pulled aside the blankets and made two cuts with a sharp clamshell across their backs so that the blood flowed freely. Some gave no sign of pain; others cried out, which was permissible. Only one attempted to look up, and the dancers beat him with their staffs. Then the head speaker said, "This is for your health; you will be healthy, you will grow strong, you will be good people. You must not look up into a tree from under its branches until these cuts have been completely healed, or the tree will never bear fruit."

Everyone moved indoors to the dancehouse, the dancers going directly to their positions. The children continued to lie on the floor, covered with their blankets during the dance and ceremony that followed. At the end of these, the dancers ran out of the dancehouse into the brush, taking with them illness from the village and from the various tribal populations. The supernaturals then returned to their supernatural home at the south end of the world.

On the morning of the fifth day the children who had undergone the scarification were assembled and driven by the dancers as rapidly as possible about the village and out into the valley. The children held one another's hands, making a continuous line. When they became fatigued they were made to lie down, and covered with branches by the dancers. There they remained throughout the day. Just after sundown they were driven about in the same manner until they were fatigued again. Again they were made to lie down, covered with branches, under which they remained until the following morning. A small brush enclosure was built just outside the dancehouse into which the children were brought and made to dance, after which the head Yomta chanted a prayer for good health and long life over them. The willow twigs that each of the children had carried were deposited in a pile; they were then free to go.

Several times throughout the Big-Time the Kuksu dancers went through the same ritual of taking away all illness, and each time the Kuksu doctor was also summoned, always coming from the south and returning to the south, like the dancers carrying away with him all disease.

Old Man, who had been sick during the past winter, was borne into the dancehouse. The Kuksu doctor was summoned and came in from the south. In the silence he danced, neither speaking nor singing, but blowing constantly on a double bone whistle, a short note followed by a long-drawn-out one. When he reached the patient he ran four times around him clockwise and four times counter-clockwise. He inserted the point of his staff under the neck of the patient and made upward-praying motions four times, repeating the motions under the shoulder, the hips, and finally the knees of the patient. Then he tapped and pressed down with his staff on the forehead, the chest, the belly, and finally the knees of the patient. Finally he ran out of the village into the hills, stopping four times, and turning his head to the left. He had carried away the illness; the patient would be well.

Chapter XXII

WITHIN the Pomo territory, the tools, implements, and utensils necessary for occupations, daily life, and specialized activities, were traded and exchanged, as well as bought and sold. The good bows, each of which commanded a price of four thousand beads, came from the north. Sea otter skins, which were rare and greatly desired throughout the region, also brought high prices. The Lake Country people especially, being so far from the coast, were the highest bidders for these skins. The area was interrelated on the trading basis not only of finished products, but raw materials. The Sulphur Bank people brought raw magnesite, as well as fired magnesite, which they exchanged for the services of the valley people, who had the knowledge and skill and power to shape the stone pieces properly and to drill holes through them without breaking them, as well as to make the drills themselves. It was in this valley too that some of the best baskets were made. To the uninitiated the trading, buying, and selling might have seemed haphazard, but there was a definite pattern to it. The people from the coast at Bodega Bay brought sea products of every sort into the interior: salt, seaweed, sea otter skins, clamshells and so on; the people from the northeast brought their bows, salt, bear-cub skins. The people from Clear Lake brought fish, mallard duck feathers, wild fowl, magnesite, and obsidian. The role of the people of the Russian River valleys was for the most part to refine the raw materials into commodities. They made rabbit blankets, fine baskets, money, quivers, and tanned leather.

In the course of routine visits and trading expeditions everything passed back and forth from the extremes of east and west, that is, from the coast and the Lake through the valleys of the Russian River.

Trading during a Big-Time went on all over the village, with everyone enjoying the exchanges of articles that were scarce in their home territories. Trading was a casual, careful, unhurried affair. Everyone knew the things that he desired and needed and was prepared with those he wished to sell or trade.

Long Haired Woman had made a beautiful feather basket, which she wanted to sell for enough money to buy a long necklace. The basket was made of iridescent green mallard feathers set in a beautiful pattern in which the yellow of flicker feathers seemed to shine and sparkle. She had got the mallard feathers in a trade the previous year with some Lake Country people. An old woman walked by, looking at it with interest, and a few others stopped to examine it. Later that day the old woman came back, stopped about twenty feet away, and said, "This is a wonderful Big-Time we are having. We will all be healthy."

"That is so," said Long Haired Woman, "and it's nice that you people have come to help us. Won't you have something to eat?"

The old woman approached and accepted graciously, without neglecting the usual precaution of taking the proffered food with her left hand first. She had some beautiful money strings hanging about her neck, which Long Haired Woman admired. The old woman responded by taking a string off her neck and handing it to Long Haired Woman.

Long Haired Woman said, "Yes, this is nice, but you have some more beautiful money."

The old woman took another string off her neck and then said, "You must make very nice baskets. You look like that kind of woman."

They both knew that Long Haired Woman had a reputation as one of the finest basket makers in the territory. Long Haired Woman lifted her feather basket to display it. The old woman examined it carefully while they chatted casually about various ordinary matters. Then Long Haired Woman said, "That small bracelet of money that you have is very nice."

The old woman decided that the two strings Long Haired Woman now had on her lap plus the bracelet would be enough. But she did not want to part with one of her two matching bracelets; she was willing to part only with her money bead necklaces even though they contained more beads than the bracelet. So she said, "Yes, this is a nice bracelet. But here is another string of beads just as nice," and she took them off her neck. Long Haired Woman considered the price right, and was satisfied. The old woman then said, "I would like this basket."

"Grandmother, you may have it as a present," said Long Haired Woman.

"That is nice, granddaughter, and I'll give you the money beads for a present." After a little more conversation the old woman departed.

As for Man of Many Beads, he had decided in advance that he needed a new bow. He had never had one of those good northern bows, and although he had been very successful in his hunting, he knew that a good bow gave a man a special distinction in the community. When the northeastern group had come into the village he had taken careful note of all of the available bows and had been particularly attracted to one obviously made with great skill and infinite patience. At a propitious moment he strolled over in a casual fashion and stood beside the family group of the men who owned the bow. After a long silence one of the visitors smiled and said, "It is kind of you people to have us here."

Man of Many Beads replied, "It is good of you people to come to help us have a Big-Time." After a period of conversation Man of Many Beads said, "That is a good bow you have there."

The stranger said, "Yes, it is a nice bow," taking up a bow other than the one Man of Many Beads wanted.

"That is a very fine bow. That is another fine one over there," said Man of Many Beads.

The stranger then strung the bow that Man of Many Beads had indicated and handed it over. Man of Many Beads tested it and said, "I would like to have this bow."

The stranger replied, "I would like to sell this bow, and I would like to have the string of money that you have."

Man of Many Beads had worn a string of 4,000 beads around his neck. Both men were content at the exchange.

The general feeling prevailed that the Big-Time was a very successful one. There would be a busy season ahead. The money manufacturers knew that they would be given many commissions to make money, and that they would receive twenty-five per cent of the finished money for themselves. They saw pieces of magnesite changing hands and knew that they would soon be polishing and finishing them, for which work they would receive payment according to the size of the pieces of magnesite. The arrowpoint and drill makers, as a professional group, were also happy, for they would not now have to travel to the Lake Area to obtain materials. They would make a good profit manufacturing arrowheads, spear points, and drills. Others were pleased to have been able to buy the bear-cub skins, which were very rare. They would manufacture these into quivers and sell them for a good price. The buying, selling, and trading had been successful all around. Each tribe had eaten foods they had not tasted for a long time; families had been reunited with their daughters and other female relatives who had married away. Additional marriages had been arranged and alliances strengthened between the various tribal groups. The people had had their dance, had sacrificed to their dead, and made offerings to the supernaturals. The mourners could now stop their mourning, and all would be healthy. A general feeling of goodwill prevailed.

The reader may feel that the whole story has not been told. It is true that the story is still going on: it will continue until the end of man. Parts of the tale may be found in the authors' articles and books listed in Bibliography B. Additional material, which pertains especially to the same period presented in this volume, may be found in Bibliography A.

Conclusion

THIS abbreviated presentation is sufficient for the reader to understand that these people were proud, self-respecting, and self-sufficient. They lived a full life with a well-established form of government, religion, and social control of all their activities and participation—including family life, war, manufacture, commerce, occupations, play groups, an economic system based on monetary denominations, and the other components of a self-perpetuating population of long standing.

Professions, occupations, and various forms of leadership for men and women required a lifetime of training and preparation. Achievement, primarily on the basis of ability, led to success, security, status, and prestige.

A number of formal men's associations were present: professional groups of fishermen, deer hunters, doctors, gamblers, and money manufacturers, as well as a men's secret society. The sweathouse in addition to being a social club where men gathered for sweating, relaxing, gossiping, and instructing the young, was the place for initiating tribal activities. The tribal council, composed of the male heads of the great families, agreed on the times for dances and get-togethers for social and religious reasons, or for the organization of war or trading parties and the issuing of invitations to tribes of neighboring valleys. On invitation from the families, it also handled the rare cases of juvenile delinquents and abberrant individuals and took action, furthermore, in drastic cases which affected the tribe.

The women, who were kept in control on a tribal basis by the men's secret society, had no associations outside the family. However, in addition to acting as assistants to the men who were the interfamily representatives and political heads of the families, there were status positions and accomplishments which they could achieve. The majority of the internal affairs of the family was under the direct control of its Head Woman, who also was the secretary-treasurer and custodian of all the valuables of all the family members. She oversaw behavior in the matter of gifts at weddings, funerals, and other interfamily contacts. She was the power within the family in regard to food-gathering, preparation, storage, and distribution.

With the exception of rough temporary carrying baskets, the women made the baskets. It is reported that they made the finest basketry in the world, some of which sold for as high as five thousand dollars apiece. Women were known and acclaimed for their excellence in this occupation.

These people had faced up to and solved many of the problems of group living, including two which remain problems in the modern world, the population explosion and therapeutic psychiatry. They had developed and imposed birth control methods whereby their population was kept within the limits of the food supply of the valley. Furthermore they had developed a variety of forms of psychological therapy whereby they were able to take care of their members without segregative institutions.

We may sum up the preceding as follows: all individuals knew their places and the procedures, endeavors, and participations leading to the achievement of status and position in this population.

The question, then, which may be asked is: What caused these people, who had lived a fully integrated life, to change so as to fit the descriptions given by some of their white neighbors?

The old man presenting his ideas summed up his reasons, including knowledge that it is man who makes, maintains, and changes his culture and his way of life, and that the changing way of life of the world was bringing about problems for all.

The earliest westerners to come to this area were males, some of whom took Pomo women as sexual partners, and in a few cases as wives. Subsequently many women were discarded and left to care for their children in a situation where their relatives were dispersed and impoverished.

The initial disruption of these people by the Spaniards, who forcibly transported men, women, and children indiscriminately to the Mission in Solano, was further accelerated by the Americans, who moved the Indians to Army reservations. In both cases the distance was considerable.

Almost every important position of power, leadership, and honor in the Pomo culture was negated or deleted by the Spaniards and early Americans. Participation in the various formal men's organizations ceased. The secret society, the sweathouse, the council composed of male heads of families, were of the past. Each man functioned as an individual with little authority and few prerogatives. Responsibility to his wife, children, elder relatives and in-laws decreased and in most cases ceased at the termination of the brittle marriages which had become the customary form of union. For the women, the elemental relationship of mother and child became important and dominant.

There eventually emerged a situation in which the Indian men were employed as cowboys, sheepherders, and on ranches in many other different capacities. Some of them achieved renown as bronco busters and cowboys.

Pomo women were employed in households as servants and nursemaids where they learned that the white women, although ostensibly subservient to their husbands, actually controlled many of the community activities, especially those related to education, social affairs, recreation, religion, law and order, and the community. In fact, it was the women who had insisted on changing what they found to be a wide-open rollicking frontier town into a respectable community. It was these white women who had been left behind in many parts of the United States while their husbands established themselves in this valley and who, in the absence of their husbands, were forced to become the actual heads of their families, taking over all of the prerogatives and duties, obligations and responsibilities of the male head in addition to their own, and who continued with them, once having become accustomed to them.

When the wives who had been left behind while the men

established themselves in California Town arrived and found that Americans were living with Indian women and that some of their husbands had participated in like fashion, they imposed severe restrictions, resulting in Pomo women not being employed in white homes. The depression of the thirties reinforced this to the point that eventually not one Indian woman nor one Pomo man was employed in town.

Although the aboriginal Pomo society was man-dominated, nevertheless, as shown earlier, the women had had positions of power and authority. These were augmented and stimulated by the period of great disruption in which they were left to take care of themselves and their children, and the contacts with the American women reinforced their dominant role. In comparison, the role of the men was minimized.

Agriculture had become commercially profitable in the valley. Prunes, pears, peaches, grapes, hops, and other items were produced for outside consumption. Both Pomo men and women worked in the fields, and each received his or her own pay. This hard money, in addition to the previous position of women, placed them in an even higher position of power in relation to the men.

The killing of one's enemies, a slow expensive procedure by means of the old forms of sorcery, was superceded by the killing by force without expense. Starvation, although a threat, was controlled by the Pomo who had learned to utilize a tremendous variety of fauna and flora, especially acorns and horse chestnuts. The latter, one of the richest foods and somewhat comparable in use to that of bread today, was no longer available to them. It was impossible for them to obtain their food directly; now they were forced to purchase it. This became a means of enslavement because they had to work at anything in order to earn money. Their previous wealth of baskets and Indian money was worth little on the open market. A fine basket which required a few months of work now sold for five or ten dollars. The Indians could borrow from their prospective employers, the ranchers, and pay back with their summer earnings, but this meant they could not work for anyone else until they had repaid what they had borrowed.

The various occupations of the Pomo Indians of the aboriginal days were one of the means whereby the elder men retained their status, prestige, power, and prerogatives. Younger men had to cater to and be subservient to the older men in order to achieve and receive from the older men that which through time aided them in accomplishing their purposes in life. However, due to the restrictions on the Indians, the expropriation of their land, and the uneconomical returns of the old occupations, there resulted little participation in the old occupations.

Participation in the western religions of Catholicism and Protestantism resulted in the negating of their own supernaturals and deleted the occupation of the religico.

When we arrived in 1934 the community was composed of a majority of whites, many of whom regarded the Indians in the stereotyped and generally derogatory terms presented earlier. The Indians lived on rancherias, each of which was some miles from town; their transporation was by horse, foot, and in a few cases by automobile. Their settlements looked forlorn, the houses were unpainted, and their communities could be summed up as being "on the wrong side of the tracks."

They were agricultural workers who were paid on a piecework basis. During the height of the harvest season they put in long hard labor from early dawn to dusk, with entire families, including the aged and the young, participating. During the slack season the general state was that of unemployment. Neither the men nor the women had any expectation of rising in status, of becoming owners of ranches, that is, of receiving rewards commensurate with their efforts. They all received the same amount of money per item, regardless of years of experience. During the harvesting season, with money more available, and despite the federal law against selling alcoholic beverages to Indians, they obtained wine and participated in group drinking for as much as three or four days at a time. In cases which we saw, the aged and youngsters also participated.

This form of drinking occurred on other occasions. It was apparent to us that it was a result of resentment against their position as compared with their aboriginal days. They voiced this in phrases such as, "They have taken away our land, they work us to death in this hot sun, and we can't earn enough to live decently."

During this period, 1934-1936, they were distinct in dress and action in town; the majority wore a type of frontier dress and the mothers carried the infants 'n baby baskets on their backs.

By this time not one full-time Indian occupation remained. Even the Chief received no recompense. On the other hand, the Indians knew the many occupations by means of which individual members of the white community achieved status and position with power, wealth, and honor in the community. But they were closed to the Indian, as well as others, unless he was able to receive not only a high school, but a college and professional education, which was beyond his aspiration at that time. No one had achieved it. Furthermore, those few who had gone away to college for a year or two, or had been employed in outside communities such as San Francisco and Sacramento, returned and participated like the other members of the community. Therefore there was little incentive for the younger members to strive for a college education.

The end result of all of this among the Indians was a public attitude of failure which, even among those who had been outstanding in high school athletics and academic achievements, ended in dissipation.

During the research an apparent anomaly appeared. The assimilation and change in participation of the Pomos occurred most rapidly during a period when their participation in California Town was almost zero. Research led to the finding that it was especially during that period that intense and intimate contact between the Indians and a large number of white migratory workers occurred during a harvest season, when the two worked side by side in the fields, orchards, and vineyards, lived in the same encampments on the ranches located outside of town, and spent much leisure time together. From this contact the Indians learned about style of dress, food and eating customs, family relations, religion, the credit system in the purchase of automobiles, habits of speech, the idea of the strike, working and living conditions in other localities, and levels of aspiration.

The white migratory workers were not merely an amorphous aggregate of individuals haphazardly working together, but rather a population with leadership, common interests and experiences, and well-established communication, although they did not constitute an organized group with an internal structure. A large number of them followed a ten-month circuit from Northern Mexico and Arizona through California, Oregon, Washington, and Canada, and spent the remaining two months on vacation or in some other occupation.

The northern California Indians who lived side by side and participated with these workers lost many of their constraints. They were no longer fearful of "poisoning" by strangers who were considered enemies. Instead, they learned about the treatment of Indians in other communities and began to realize that their well-being had its base in mutuality, independently of their own community affiliation.

By this time, 1939-41, the Indian women had formed an association, the "Pomo Mothers' Club." The officers, consisting of an elected president, vice president, secretary, and treasurer, met twice a month. The members held monthly meetings. The primary purpose was to provide leadership, guidance, and supervision of all Indians in the area. The women were concerned with the increase in deviational behavior in the younger generation, especially in regard to alcohol, sex, and the general negativism to the elders and family life.

They planned and organized a variety of activities which included individuals outside the tribal group. For example, they met with townswomen's groups and sponsored trips to neighboring white communities to present Pomo arts and crafts. They also planned intertribal and tribal affairs, decided when dances were to be held, and when neighboring groups were to be invited. Dances were scheduled monthly or oftener, depending on the season.

The club not only became the important means of contact between Indians and members of white communities, but also dealt with governmental officials on such matters as hot school lunches for children, aid for non-ward Indians, and community welfare. Attendance at the dances was by family, including babes in arms and aged men and women.

The dances aided considerably in reestablishing communal interrelations and some control of the deviational activities which had become rather general in the population, especially in the teenage group.

By this time the women had become dominant and provided the image of a matriarchal society. The very solution of leadership by women demoted the leadership of the men, somewhat as has occurred in other minority groups, for example the Negro and Puerto Rican today.

However, if anything, the situation of the Pomo Indians at that time was worse. Aside from contact with the harvesters and with outside communities it was a ghetto life for the Indian in Deep Valley. Not one Indian worked in town, and when he purchased food or other articles in stores, he waited on the side until the whites had been served. On their rancherias modern facilities were practically non-existent. They had no running water, electricity, or toilets in the home. A tremendous amount of time was wasted due to their lack of cooking and bathing facilities, despite which they had retained their habits of cleanliness; they bathed at least once a day.

It was during this period that the Indian Reorganization Act was made law and was followed by meetings of the mature males with government officials. This provided the older men with some leadership status in the community and a greater understanding of legal procedure. One Indian leader became a member of the grand jury in town and, with the support of a number of white townspeople sympathetic to the Indians and who firmly believed in their deserving and being given opportunities, eventuated in the Indians employing an attorney in a court action involving their position in the community. The incident which sparked the long-smouldering condition was that of a young Indian girl being told to move from the orchestra to the balcony of the movie theater.

The turning point was the settlement of the case before it went to trial. The restrictions were removed, following which the Indians sat in the orchestra, could go to any restaurant, went to beauty parlors and barber shops, and in general participated in the community. The transition from a segregated to a desegregated situation was accomplished with little trouble. The success of this was shared by both the townspeople and the Indians.

On our return the following summer many townspeople spoke with pride about the changes.

By the summer of 1946, it was almost impossible to distinguish Indian from white in town, except that more whites than Indians had fair skins. Many of the Indian houses were freshly painted; some had lawns, washing machines, oil furnaces, and radios. Almost all of them had automobiles. The women had permanents, wore slacks, wheeled their babies in carriages; and the men wore sports coats and slacks. The majority of the young Indians had gone to school, many had graduated from high school, and some were attending college. A number of them had jobs in town.

The Indian had increased his mobility. It was the exceptional one who had not been to San Francisco, Sacramento, and more distant places. A large number of them had been in the armed forces where they had been treated with honor because they were Indians and also because they excelled. Many of the women had worked in shipyards and other war industries along with the men who were unable to get into uniform. The GI benefits were utilized to go to college and to borrow money. Some purchased land in the valley proper, thereby moving away from the ghetto and increasing their participation in commercial agriculture. Indians were employed as automobile mechanics, one girl was an usher in the only movie house in town, and there were other employments. A large industry moved into the area, necessitating the building of homes, roads, and other structures, which resulted in a shortage of labor and employment of Indians.

Furthermore, the depression was over. During the war years outsiders began moving into the community, a movement which increased in numbers after the war. Meanwhile many of the old timers, both Indian and white, had died. The net result was a dilution of tensions.

By this time Filipino men had come into the Pomo territory as harvest hands. Some of them married Pomo women and set up households which were located neither in town nor on the rancherias. The Indians took over the prejudice of some of the whites and in turn treated the Filipinos negatively. Some of the

Indian families were shamed and had nothing to do with their own daughters married to Filipinos. It was an interesting situation, especially since the wives of the Filipino men were treated with the utmost respect and consideration by their husbands who did not allow them to work. The Filipino men, on the basis of their communication with one another all over the state, were seldom unemployed and earned bonus wages because of their expertness and regular work habits. They owned modern cars, dressed neatly, seldom drank. Nevertheless, at certain social affairs in a different part of the area, the tension rose to the point where knifings occurred. And in California Town, during the summer of 1947, the town police were present at all social affairs attended by Filipinos and Indians. However, this situation was resolved, leading to an integration which was mutually beneficial.

This aided in emphasizing the position of men in the Indian population.

The Mormons during this time were actively engaged in bringing the Indians, nominally Catholics, into the Mormon Church. The Indians were already participating in the Pentecostal religion.

It was also during this time that automation was increased. Hop-picking machines were developed which were beginning to displace the Indian who had depended on that activity for high wages and a form of social life during the summer.

The changes in participation and in Indian-white relations occurred for at least three reasons. First, the Indians imitated the whites and learned from them outside of their own community by contacts with the harvesters and going to other communities. They learned about legal procedures and initiated them. Second, the death of older members of both the white and Indian communities, along with the increase in the white population from other areas, diluted public opinion on both sides. And, third, there were increased opportunities resulting from the postwar economic situation and the shortage of labor, plus the GI Bill and the training received during the war.

We may sum up the change as follows. When the Indians were not allowed to participate with the whites, they could not become participating members of the white way of life. There were white men who did not comprehend this and criticized and condemned the Indians for what they had been forced to become, and then attempted to increase the restrictions. There were those who had no interest in ascertaining what the Indians had been like. On the other hand, when the Indians were allowed to participate one became a member of the grand jury and in high school some of them excelled, one becoming valedictorian, and still others succeeded in occupations following which they were respected for their achievements.

There is no question but that increased earnings, that is, economic factors, had aided in the change. However it is incorrect to accept money per se as the solution because it is only one of the means whereby participation was increased. Choice of participation must be included and the Indian chose improvement.

It is interesting that during the period 1946-1948 one heard the same complaints by white townspeople about their own children which had been heard previously from Indians in regard to their children. They were about drinking, sexual indulgence, and lack of respect for parents and elders. They included breakdown in the family, religion, consideration for other members of the community, for laws, and in general the deviational forms of behavior ascribed to teenagers across the country.

The complaints were almost the same as those voiced by the elder Indian in the introduction to this book in regard to the Indians and to the whites.

The insights of the old Indian could be considered a warning as to what was occurring as the result of the disintegration of self-sufficient community living which was being accelerated by man in the world at large. In fact, the way of life of the Indian before contact with the westerners was somewhat like the village life of the majority of the people of the world just after World War II. Communities were becoming integrated with the total world economy which consisted of specialized endeavors, success in which depended on what occurred in other parts of the world rather than in one's own community. And therefore the control of individuals in each community by the members of the community was changing rapidly.

To have expected California Town to have solved these problems in regard to the Indians or their own families is to have expected more from them than has been achieved anywhere else.

In both tribal and village life the elders of the family were the repository of knowledge and skills; they imparted them to the younger members who were enabled to achieve status and position. It was the elders who had knowledge of their history, religion, medicine, who provided food, discipline, and other care. Today the schools, colleges, and libraries have supplanted them. Today the young return from school and college and teach their elders. This in effect not only creates a false impression in the minds of the younger people, but takes away the confidence of the elders. The result is that it carries over to the wisdom of the elders, who, because they do not have knowledge of science and the world therefore are also thought to be lacking in wisdom.

Today the various institutions developed by man provide the services previously provided by the family. Doctors and hospitals provide health care; stores supply food, clothing, and drugs; schools, knowledge and skills; labor unions, employment; the government, care of the unemployed and the aged. In fact, from birth to death there are institutions which have supplanted the family. Therefore one cannot expect the family to remain unchanged. In addition, greater opportunities for advancement in places other than one's home community have resulted in the movement to the cities and the family becoming minimal in size.

World changes affecting community living are accelerating to the point where the situation is incomprehensible to the majority of our leaders. One example should suffice to make the point. Automation is replacing occupations so rapidly that it is almost impossible to provide guidance for the young. The acceleration and multiplication of occupations and professions, religions, forms of recreation, and other participations is such that preparing for life means a comprehension of participating at a future time when the world will be rather different from that in which the individual is being prepared.

We may conclude that until comprehension is achieved, the solution to the living togetherness, regardless of ancestral groups, is dependent on the understanding of accelerated change.

The insight provided by a study of the Pomos is that solutions to problems in any one community without understanding the modern world are impossible. In Deep Valley, separated from the total world of man, there had lived a population which had been self-sufficient. Initially the early westerners also developed a self-sufficient community. But within a relatively short period of time they also had to adjust to the changes in the outside world in regard to food, lumber, and other items which were produced in the valley, and also to war and other world situations beyond their control. Furthermore, the development of all kinds and varieties of specializations and institutions affected their daily lives. To solve the problems in this or any other community requires the inclusion of the accelerated items which impinge on the community.

Bibliography

ABBREVIATIONS USED

AA	*American Anthropologist*
AMNH-B	American Museum of Natural History, *Bulletin*
BAE-B	Bureau of American Ethnology, *Bulletin*
BAE-AR	Bureau of American Ethnology, *Annual Report*
CUSNH	Contributions from the U.S. National Herbarium
CNAE	Contributions to North American Ethnology
ELA	Essays in Anthropology in Honor, A. L. Kroeber
HAV	Holmes Anniversary Volume
JAFL	*Journal of American Folklore*
MAI, HF-IN	Museum, American Indian, Heye Foundation, Notes
MPM-B	Milwaukee Public Museum, *Bulletin*
MPM-Y	Milwaukee Public Museum, *Yearbook*
OM	*Overland Monthly*
OW	*Out West*
UC-AR	University of California, Anthropology Records
UC-PAAE	University of California Publications in Archaeology and Ethnology
USNM-R	United States National Museum, *Report*

A. REFERENCES

Alley, Bowen & Company: History of Mendocino County, California; San Francisco, 1880.

Bailey, G.: Special Agent Interior Department—Report Commissioner of Indian Affairs for 1858.

Bancroft, H. H.: Native Races, I, III; San Francisco, 1886; History of California, II; San Francisco, 1886.

Barrett, S. A.: A New Moquelumnan Territory in California; American Anthropologist n. s. VI, 1904

———, The Pomo in the Sacramento Valley of California. AA, ns, 6:189, 190, 1904

————, Basket Designs of the Pomo Indians. AA, ns, 7:648-653, 1905

————, A Composite Myth of the Pomo Indians. JAFL, 19:37-51, 1906

————, The Ethno-geography of the Pomo and Neighboring Indians. UC-PAAE, 6:1-332, 1908A

————, Pomo Indian Basketry. UC-PAAE, 7:133-306, 1908B

————, Pomo Buildings. HAV, 1-17. Washington, D.C., 1916

————, Ceremonies of the Pomo Indians. UC-PAAE, 12:397-441, 1917A

————, Pomo Bear Doctors. UC-PAAE, 12:443-465, 1917B

————, The Wintun Hesi Ceremony. UC-PAAE, 14:437-488, 1919

————, Progress in the Museum's Group Building Program. MPM-Y, 10:187-199, 1932

————, Pomo Myths. MPM-B, 15:1-608, 1933

————, The Army Worm: a Food of the Pomo Indians. EIA, 1-5, 1936

Barrett, S. A. and Gifford, E. W. Miwok Material Culture. MPM-B, 2:117-376, 1933

Beach, W. W.: The Indian Miscellany; Albany, 1877

Bowers, H. B.: Second Edition. Map of Sonoma County, California . . . with additions and corrections to September 1, 1882

Brackenridge, N. B.: Official Map of Mendocino County, California; San Francisco, 1887

Browne, J. Ross: The Indian Reservations of California; Harper's Magazine for August, 1861—Beach's Indian Miscellany; Albany, 1877

Carter, C. F.: The Missions of Nueva California; San Francisco, 1900

Chestnut, V. K.: Plants used by the Indians of Mendocino County, California; United States Department of Agriculture, Division of Botany; Contributions from the United States National Herbarium, VII, No. 3

————, Plants Used by the Indians of Mendocino County, California. CUSNH, 7:295-408, 1902

Cope, Leona.: Calendars of the Indians North of Mexico. UC-PAAE, 16:119-176, 1919

Culin, Stewart.: Games of the North American Indians. BAE-AR, 24:1-846, 1907

Dixon, R. B.: Basketry Designs of the Indians of Northern California. AMNH-B, 17:1-32, 1902

Dixon, R. B. and Kroeber, A. L.: Numerical Systems of the Languages of California. AA, ns, 9:663-690, 1907

Dodge, George M.: Official Map of Marin County, California; San Francisco, 1892

Drake, Sir Francis: Early English Voyages to the Pacific Coast of America (from their own, and contemporary English accounts). Sir Francis Drake.—Out West, XVIII; Los Angeles, California, 1903

Engelhardt, Fr. Zephyrin, O.S.F.: The Franciscans in California; Harbor Springs, Michigan, 1897

Essene, Frank: Culture Element Distributions: XXI, Round Valley. UC-AR, 8:1-97, 1942

Ford, Captain H. L., Sub-agent in charge of the Mendocino Reservation: Report of, to Thomas J. Henley, Superintendent of Indian Affairs for California; in Report of the Commissioner of Indian Affairs for the year 1856

Deposition of Captain H. L. Ford, taken February 22, 1860—State of California Legislature, Majority and Minority Reports of the Special Joint Committee on the Mendocino War, 1860

Gibbs, George: "Journal of the Expedition of Colonel Redick M'Kee," United States Indian Agent, through Northwestern California. Performed in the Summer and Fall of 1851, Schoolcraft, Archives of Aboriginal Knowledge, III

——, Journal of Expedition of Colonel Redick M'Kee . . . through Northwestern California . . . in 1851, In Schoolcraft, Indian Tribes, 3:99-177, Philadelphia, 1853

Gifford, E. W.: Pomo Lands on Clear Lake. UC-PAAE, 20:77-94, 1923

——, Clear Lake Pomo Society. UC-PAAE, 18:287-390, 1926

——, California Balanophagy. EIA, 87-98, 1936

Gifford, E. W. and Kroeber, A. L.: Culture Element Distributions: IV, Pomo. UC-PAAE, 37:117-254, 1937

Gloss.: Glossary in "Pomo Myths," MPM-B, 15:494-548, 1933

Goddard, Professor P. E.: The Kato Pomo not Pomo; American Anthropologist, n.s. V., 1903

Hakulyt, Richard: The Voyages, Navigations, Traffiques, and Discoveries of the English Nation; London, 1600

——, Reprinted edition of the above; London, 1810

Henderson, Wm. and Aginsky, B. W.,: A Social Science Field Laboratory. ASR, 6:41-44, 1941

Heye, George G.: A Pomo Feather Sash. MAI, HF-IN, 5:443-445, 1928

Hildreth, William J.: Deposition of William J. Hildreth, taken February 24, 1860—State of California Legislature, Majority and Minority Reports of the Special Joint Committee on the Mendocino War, 1860

Hittell, Theodore H.: History of California, I; San Francisco, 1885
Holmes, W. H.: Anthropological Studies in California. USNM-R:155-188, 1902
Hudson, J. W.: Pomo Basket Makers. OM (2d. ser.), 21:561-578, 1893
——, Pomo Wampum Makers. OM (2d ser.), 30:101-108, 1897
——, Preparation of Acorn Meal by the Pomo Indians. AA, ns, 2:775, 776, 1900
King, M. G., and Morgan, T. W.: Map of the Central Portion of Napa Valley and the Town of St. Helena; San Francisco, 1881
Kniffen, Fred B.: Pomo Geography. UC-PAAE, 36:353-400, 1939
Kroeber, A. L.: Basket Designs of the Indians of Northwestern California; University of California Publications, Archaeology and Ethnology, 11, 1905
——, The Coast Yuki of California; American Anthropologist n.s. V, 1903
——, The Dialectic Divisions of the Moquelumnan Family in Relation to the Internal Differentiation of the Other Linguistic Families of California; American Anthropologist n.s. VIII, 1906.
——, California Basketry and the Pomo. AA, ns, 11:233-249, 1909
——, California Place Names of Indian Origin. UC-PAAE, 12:31-69, 1916
——, California Culture Provinces. UC-PAAE, 17:151-169, 1920
——, Elements of Culture in Native California. UC-PAAE, 13:259-328, 1922
——, Handbook of the Indians of California. BAE-B, 78:1-995. Pomo section, pp. 222-271, 1925
——, Yuki Myths. A, 27:910-915, 1932
——, Culture Element Distributions: XV, Salt, Dogs, Tobacco. UC-AR, 6:1-20, 1941
Lacock, Dryden: Deposition of Dryden Lanock; taken February 25, 1860—State of California Legislature, Majority and Minority Reports of the Special Joint Committee on the Mendocino War, 1860
Latham, Dr. R. G.: Transactions of the Philological Society of London, 1856
——, Elements of Comparative Philology; London, 1862
Loeb, E. M.: Pomo Folkways. UC-PAAE, 19:149-405, 1926.
The Western Kuksu Cult. UC-PAAE, 33:1-178, 1932
Mason, O. T.: Primitive Travel and Transportation. USNM-R: 237-593, 1894
——, Cradles of the American Indians. USNM-9: 161-212, 1897
——, Aboriginal American Basketry. USNMR:117-548, 1902

McAidie, Alexander G.: Climatology of California, United States Weather Bureau Bulletin, L, 1903

McKee, John: Minutes kept by John McKee, secretary on the expedition from Sonoma, through Northern California—Senate Executive Documents, Special Session, 32nd Congress, March, 1853, Document 4

Menefee, C. A.: Historical and Descriptive Sketch Book of Napa, Sonoma, Lake, and Mendocino; Napa City, 1873

Mineral Map of Lake County, California. Issued by the California State Mining Bureau, Lewis E. Aubury, State Mineralogist.

Merrill, R. E.: Plants used in Basketry by the California Indians. UC-PAAE, 20:215-242, 1923

Morgan, L. H.: Houses and House Life of the American Aborigines. CNAE, 4:1-281, 1881

Orchard, W. C.: A Pomo Headdress. MAI, HF-IN, 4:170-174, 1927

Pearson, T. Gilbert (Ed).: Birds of America. Garden City Pub. Co., New York, 1936

Powell, Major J. W.: Indian Linguistic Families of America North of Mexico. 7th Annual Report Bureau American Ethnology, 1885-86

Powers, Stephen: Tribes of California, Contributions to North American Ethnology, III, 1877

———, The North California Indians, Overland Monthly; San Francisco, 1872-74

Purdy, Carl: Pomo Indian Baskets and Their Makers; in Land of Sunshine, XV; Los Angeles, 1901, and Out West, XVI; Los Angeles, 1902

———Mr. Purdy's reprinted edition, in book form, Los Angeles, 1902

Simmons, Miss Kathryn: Traditions and Landmarks of Yolo; Woodland Daily Democrat, February 16, 1905

Slocum, Bowen, & Company: History of Napa and Lake Counties, California; San Francisco, 1881

Stewart, O. C.: Notes on Pomo Ethnogeography. UC-PAAE, 40:29-62, 1943

Taylor, Alexander S.: Indianology of California, in The California Farmer; San Francisco, 1860-61

Thompson, Robert A.: Historical and Descriptive Sketch of Sonoma County, California; Philadelphia, 1877

———, Central Sonoma; San Francisco, 1884

———, The Russian Settlement in California Known as Fort Ross; Santa Rosa, 1896

Tuthill, Franklin: History of California; San Francisco, 1866

Voc.: Vocabulary in "The Ethno-geography of the Pomo and Neighboring Indians." UC-PAAE, 6:56-68, 1908

Von Baer, K. E. and Gr. Von Helmersen: Beitrage zur Kenntniss des Russischen Reiches, I; St. Petersburg, 1839

Von Kotzebue, Otto: A Voyage of Discovery into the South Sea and Beering's Straits, for the purpose of Exploring the Northwest Passage, London, 1821

————, A New Voyage Round the World; London, 1830

West, G. A.: Tobacco, Pipes, and Smoking Customs of the American Indians. MPM-B, 17:1-994, 1934

Wiley, Austin: Report, Commissioner of Indian Affairs, in Report Secretary of the Interior, 1864, in House Executive Documents, 1864-65, V, No. 1

B. AUTHOR PUBLICATIONS

Aginsky, B. W.: *Mechanics of Kinship*, American Anthropologist, Vol. 37, No. 3, July-September 1935

————, *Time Levels in Societal Analysis*, American Anthropologist, Vol. 41, No. 3, July-September 1939

————, *Psychopathic Trends in Culture*, Character and Personality, Vol. 7, No. 4, June 1939

————, *Population Control in the Shanel (Pomo) Tribe*, American Sociological Review, Vol. 4, No. 2, April 1939

————, *Interacting Forces in the Maori Family*, American Anthropologist, Vol. 42, No. 2, April-June 1940 (with Peter H. Buck)

————, *An Indian Soliloquy*, American Journal of Sociology, Vol. 46, No. 1, July 1940

————, *The Socio-Psychological Significance of Death Among the Pomo Indians*, American Imago, June 1940

————, *Methodology in the Social Sciences*, page 61, reprinted in, Selected Papers of B. W. and E. G. Aginsky, contains the methodology developed during the study. 1940

————, *A Social Science Field Laboratory*, American Sociological Review, Vol. 6, No. 1, February 1941 (with W. Henderson)

————, *Acculturation*, Proceedings of the Eighth American Scientific Congress, Vol. 2, Anthropological Sciences, Department of State, Washington, D.C., 1942

————, *Indian-White Relations: An Interdisciplinary Case Study of a California Situation: Methods and Findings*, in "Indians of the United States," contributions by members of the delegation, and by advisers, to the Policy Board of the National Inter-American Conference of Indian Life, convened at Cuzco, Peru, June 24-July 4, 1949

————, *The Interactions of Ethnic Groups:* A Case Study of Indians and Whites, American Sociological Review, Vol. 14, No. 2, April 1949

————, *Inter-Cultural Relations of Ethnic Groups.* Mimeographed and distributed 1950

————, *The Fragmentation of the American Community,* Journal of Educational Sociology, November 1952. Special Issue, Symposium, "Toward Community Improvement"

————, *This Man Made World.* Rinehart and Company, New York, 1949. Chapters IX and X contain a presentation of the research techniques used in the study and also the methodology.

Aginsky, B. W. and E. G. *A Resultant of Intercultural Relations,* Social Forces, Vol. 26, No. 1, October 1946

————, *The Process of Change in Family Types: A Case Study.* American Anthropologist, Oct.-Dec. 1949 Vol. 51 No. 4

————, *The Pomo: A Case Study of Gambling.* The Annals of the American Academy of Political and Social Science, May 1959, Vol. 269

Aginsky, Ethel G.: "Language and Culture." *Proceedings of the Eighth American Scientific Congress,* Vol. 2, Anthropological Sciences, Department of State, Washington, D.C., 1942 (pp. 271-276)

Aginsky, B. W. and E. G.: *Selected Papers of B. W. and E. G. Aginsky.* Printing Unlimited, New York, 1955. The above listed items have been brought together in this volume.

Aginsky, Burt W.: *The Bio-Social Laws of Society,* University Microfilms, Ann Arbor, Michigan, Volume XV, No. 12, 1955.

Aginsky, Burt W. and Ethel G.: *Deep Valley: A Presentation of the Pomo Indians,* University Microfilms, Ann Arbor, Michigan, Vol. XVIII, No. 2, 1958.

Aginsky, Burt W.: *A Solution to Kinship and Social Organization and A Theory of Human Genetic Systems,* University Microfilms, Ann Arbor, Michigan, Vol. XVIII, No. 2, 1958.

Aginsky, B. W. and E. G.: "Lateralizations Among American Indians." *Proceedings of the 32nd International Congress of Americanists,* Munksgaard, Copenhagen, 1958 (pp. 141-47)

Aginsky, B. W.: "Marriage, Incest, and Genetics." *Proceedings of the 32nd International Congress of Americanists,* Munksgaard, Copenhagen, 1958. (pp. 595-8)

Aginsky, B. W.: "The Evolution of American Indian Cultures, a Method and Theory." *Proceedings of the 32nd International Congress of Americanists,* Munksgaard, Copenhagen, 1958 (pp. 79-87)

Aginsky, B. W.: "The Pomo." *Encyclopedia Brittanica,* 1961.

Aginsky, B. W.: "The Psychic Unity of Mankind." *Main Currents,* Vol. 20, No. 4. 1964.